American Language Hub

LEVEL 5B
Workbook

with Key + access to Audio

macmillan education

Macmillan Education
4 Crinan Street
London N1 9XW
A division of Macmillan Education Limited

Companies and representatives throughout the world

American Language Hub Level 5B Workbook with Key
ISBN 978-1-380-04761-8
American Language Hub Level 5B Workbook with Key + access to Audio
ISBN 978-1-380-04755-7

Written by Signature Manuscripts

Signature Manuscripts has asserted their right to be identified as the author of this work in accordance with the Copyright, Designs and Patents Act 1988.

First published 2020

Original design by emc design ltd
Page make-up by SPi Global
Cover design based on original design by Restless
Cover photograph by plainpicture/Cavan Images, Getty Images/Luís Henrique Boucault
Picture research by Emily Taylor

The authors and publishers would like to thank the following for permission to reproduce their photographs:

Alamy p67; **EyeEm**/Amit Goldstein p71(a); **Getty Images**//Benoitb p43(tr), Getty Images/Chris Bennett p56, Getty Images/Rimma Bondarenko p57(c), Getty Images/Caiaimage/Paul Bradbury p54, Getty Images/Caiaimage/Agnieszka Olek p41, Getty Images/Amos Chapple p39(tl), Getty Images/Cultura p50, Getty Images/Cultura/Frank and Helena p61, Getty Images/DigitalVision p95(2), Getty Images/Adam Gault p45, Getty Images/Geber86 p59, Getty Images/Mike Harrington p52(mr), Getty Images/Hero Images pp42, 46(tr), Getty Images/Jon Hicks p71(c), Getty Images/Insights p43(tl), Getty Images/iStockphoto pp46(tl), 48, Getty Images/Istetiana p57(d), Getty Images/Jacobs Stock Photography Ltd p64, Getty Images/Johner RF p46(b), Getty Images/Kanawa_Studio p68, Getty Images/Aleksi Koskinen p70, Getty Images/Justin Lambert p60, Getty Images/Justin Lewis p51, Getty Images/Matthias Makarinus p40, Getty Images/OatmealStories p57(b), Getty Images/Kiszon Pascal pp63, 71(b), Getty Images/PeopleImages p55, Getty Images/PhotoDisc p58, Getty Images/Rawpixel p66(tr), Getty Images/SolStock p69, Getty Images/TommL p53, Getty Images/Claudia Totir p57(a), Getty Images/Vtwinpixel p52(tl), Getty Images/Westend61 p62, Getty Images/Zero Creatives p44; **Anna McNuff**/Peter Race p39(bl); **Shutterstock**/Vasyl Shulga p66(tl)

Printed and bound in Mexico
by Compañía Editorial Ultra, S.A. de C.V.

2021 2020
04 03 02 01

Contents

VOCABULARY

Journeys and adventures; Three-part phrasal verbs

A Complete the text with the words in the box.

beaten embarked globetrotters heart impenetrable long-haul provisions uncharted

Around the globe in 80 days

Around the globe in 80 days? Well the 19th-century journalist Nellie Bly did it in 72 days. But role models for intrepid female adventurers aren't confined to history books. The image of 19th-century explorers fighting their way through [1] ______ terrain and large expeditions into dangerous and [2] ______ territories is being replaced by solo modern-day adventurers and [3] ______.

Anna McNuff [4] ______ on a seven-month cycle ride into the [5] ______ of the US. She crossed every state, traveling 11,000 miles on a pink bike. She had to deal with the various challenges, including weather (cold, wind, floods and blizzards) and wild animals. In 2015, she ditched the bike and ran about 1,900 miles to complete the Te Araroa Trail in New Zealand. While water wasn't a problem, she sometimes had to carry essential [6] ______ (like chocolate!) to last for up to seven days.

While we can certainly learn from the spirit of past adventurers who endured difficult conditions to explore their world, we shouldn't forget modern-day female role models and the amazing adventures that are being had right now. And with the advent of more affordable [7] ______ flights, getting off the [8] ______ track is more possible than ever.

B Complete the sentences with one word in each blank.

1 I need a vacation to help me switch ______ from work for a while.

2 I'm playing tennis tomorrow morning at eight o'clock. Are you up ______ it?

3 Carol is always talking about cleaning up her desk, but she never seems to get ______ to it.

4 If you come up ______ any problems, just call me.

5 When you look ______ on your schooldays, do you think of them as a happy time?

6 Nobody found ______ about the missing money until the thief had left the country.

7 The best way to brush ______ on your French is to spend some time in France.

8 The problem with having a cell phone and a computer at home is that there's no getting away ______ work.

GRAMMAR
Past modals of speculation and deduction

A Choose the correct options to complete the sentences.

1 He *can't* / *mustn't* have been serious about leaving – he loves it here.
2 She *must* / *might* have mentioned it, but I really don't remember.
3 It's highly *likely* / *distinct* that the bad weather contributed to the accident.
4 Sandra *may have decided* / *may decided* to turn back because of the snow on the road.
5 Some people say the pyramids must *had* / *have* been built using very advanced technology.
6 There's a distinct *probability* / *possibility* that the explorer died of some kind of disease.
7 You *could* / *must* have seen that movie – everyone knows it!
8 He *may well* / *well may* have called me – I've had my phone turned off all morning.

B Complete the second sentence so that it has a similar meaning to the first sentence. Use three words including the word given in bold.

1 There's a good chance he has decided not to come because of the weather.
WELL
He ______________ decided not to come because of the weather.
2 I think he probably changed his mind about applying for the job.
EXTREMELY
It's ______________ he changed his mind about applying for the job.
3 I'm sure they got out of the building.
LEFT
They ______________ the building safely.
4 It's possible that Andrea forgot where we live.
MIGHT
Andrea ______________ where we live.
5 It's very likely that he fell asleep.
DISTINCT
There's ______________ that he fell asleep.
6 I'm certain it wasn't me who called you. I would remember.
CAN'T
I would remember calling you, so it ______________ me.

PRONUNCIATION
Showing your attitude

A Read the sentences aloud, paying attention to the way you pronounce the underlined phrases.

1 <u>Well, in general</u>, I agree with most of the changes to our contracts, <u>but the question is</u>, can we afford to live on the wages they're offering?
2 <u>Allegedly</u>, he got the job because his father is friends with the manager. <u>The main thing is</u>, he is pretty good at it, so that might just be a rumor.
3 <u>Supposedly</u>, the money's going to come from the sale of one of the smaller companies – <u>the question is</u>, which one?
4 <u>On the whole</u>, I think the project has been successful. <u>Surely</u>, management must be pleased with it.

6.1 **B Listen to the sentences from Exercise A. Practice saying the sentences in the same way as the speakers do in the recording.**

GRAMMAR
-*ing* and infinitive forms

A Complete the text with the correct form of the verbs in parentheses.

Finding sources you can trust

For the curious mind (and for those minds paid to be curious), the internet is an amazing tool. Researchers and journalists have access to stories across business, politics and humor. And the public has gotten used to [1] ________ (*read*) online. But in some cases, fake stories are circulated on purpose.

It's just so easy [2] ________ (*spread*) a story these days – whether it's true or false. Before the internet, most news came via newspapers which had a reputation [3] ________ (*maintain*), so they would at least take care not [4] ________ (*do*) too much that damaged their credibility. But now, with both the speed at which stories are being written and shared and the ease with which fake news can be spread online, we may have difficulty [5] ________ (*tell*) the difference between credible and questionable news.

B Match the beginnings of the sentences (1–6) to the endings (a–f).

1 When I have guests, I always worry that there's not enough food ____
2 I don't think you'll get into trouble for ____
3 Is this a good time ____
4 Have fun ____
5 There are a lot of online resources ____
6 In your opinion, is there any point ____

a surfing, but don't take any risks.
b to help you.
c to go around.
d being five minutes late.
e to talk to you about my essay?
f waiting to see the manager today?

C Choose the option which is closest in meaning to the sentence.

1 They stopped to analyze the data.
   a They were analyzing data, then stopped.
   b They were doing something else, then started analyzing data.
2 She remembered to heat the liquid.
   a She remembered something she needed to do.
   b She had the memory of doing something.

VOCABULARY
Binomial expressions

A Complete the binomial expressions with the words in the box. There are three extra words that you do not need to use.

away by greet order quiet soul sound take tear there tidy

1 When we go to the country, we like to sit and enjoy the peace and ________.
2 ________ and large, my job gives me everything I need.
3 Every relationship needs a little give and ________.
4 The boss always comes early to meet and ________ people when there's an event.
5 That was far and ________ the best movie I've ever seen!
6 The job of the police is to uphold law and ________.
7 Keeping the work area clean and ________ is a matter of safety, too.
8 There's a little wear and ________, but you'd expect that on a ten-year-old car.

B Complete the binomial expressions with two words in each blank.

1 We searched far ________ for the phone, but it was gone.
2 His is a real rags-________ story – they weren't rich as children.
3 When he plays soccer, he really puts his heart ________ into the game.
4 Time ________, they get the work wrong, even after I've shown them.
5 Frank had worked two shifts back ________ so he was exhausted.
6 It didn't happen right away. Slowly ________, I got used to living here though.
7 We watched a grandfather and grandson walk side ________ down the lane.
8 Why is she getting so upset? It's not a life-________ situation – she's just deciding which outfit to wear!

PRONUNCIATION
Pauses and pitch in presentations

A Read the beginning of a presentation and mark a (/) in red where you would take a pause. Also think about where you would step up to a higher pitch to start a new topic or step down to a lower pitch to end a topic.

I'd like to talk to you today about the bad side of staying informed. I don't mean for one minute to suggest that you should stay uninformed – it's good to keep up-to-date with what's happening – but too much news causes us stress, and that's official! Studies suggest that many of us check headlines on an hourly basis, and now experts are telling us that's not good for our state of mind, our sleep patterns or even our relationships. One of the biggest dangers is that the news, in order to hold our attention, has to be shocking. Now, I like to see an action or a horror movie occasionally, but imagine that level of tension *all* the time. Our nerves just wouldn't take it. And yet that's just what happens when we are constantly plugged in to continuous news stories. The least we should do is to make sure we don't watch the news just before going to bed. At least that might help us to sleep better at night, which in turn will help us cope with everything else.

6.2 **B Listen to someone reading the text from Exercise A. Does the speaker pause and change pitch in the same places as you? Now practice reading the presentation with the same pauses and pitch changes as the speaker in the recording.**

READING

A PREDICT Look at the pictures and the title of the article. What information will the article include? What questions will it answer?

B Read *Mungo Park: the last adventure*. Were your predictions in Exercise A correct?

C READ FOR DETAIL Read the article again and answer the questions.

1 Why was Mungo Park chosen to lead his first expedition to Africa?

2 Which two things caused him to abandon his first expedition?

3 What can we understand about Park's personality from his communication with home?

4 What happened to the people who went looking for Mungo Park?

D REFLECT Think about the answers to these questions.

1 What makes people undertake dangerous expeditions?

2 What motivates modern-day explorers to follow in the footsteps of older explorers?

Mungo Park: THE LAST ADVENTURE

Mungo Park was a young Scottish explorer who went in search of the Niger River in West Africa. After training to be a surgeon, he traveled to South-East Asia as a ship's medical officer. While in the region, he studied the plant and animal life of Sumatra and, on his return, described several new species of fish and plants that he had recorded. This gained him a certain amount of recognition and, when the African Association was looking for someone to head an expedition to explore the course of the Niger River, Park was an obvious choice.

MUNGO PARK.

His first African expedition therefore began in 1795 and Park followed the Gambia River for 200 miles (about 320 km), entering into unknown territory as he encountered the Senegal River. He was then taken prisoner for four months before escaping and eventually reaching his target, the Niger River. Lack of supplies meant that he was only able to follow it for 80 miles (about 128 km) and, on turning back, he became seriously ill. When he finally made it back to Britain in 1797, he wrote *Travels in the Interior Districts of Africa*, which was popular and helped to further his reputation.

In 1805, he was commissioned for a second expedition to chart the course of the Niger River. This expedition was dogged by misfortune from the start. Forty men set off from the Gambia in the rainy season – the worst time to do so. By the time they reached the Niger, only 11 men remained alive. However, Park made no mention of these tragic events in the letters which he sent home. He was determined to complete the expedition and set off from Bamako along the unmapped stretch of the Niger.

Eventually, a party was sent to find out what could have happened to Park and his men. Isaaco, a local guide, was hired to help them. Given that they had set out in the rainy season, might their canoes have been caught in rapids and overturned or broken against rocks and the men drowned? Had they run out of provisions? Despite being well-armed, could they have been attacked and overcome by a hostile tribe? Or could they have died of disease or been the prey of wild animals? Although death was the most likely outcome, and with no trace of Park, there were still many rumors back in Britain claiming that he had survived.

Isaaco managed to find a man named Amadi, one of Park's guides, who gave his account of events. They had been attacked several times by men in canoes and they had, as expected, encountered dangerous rapids, which they survived until they reached the rapids at Bussa where the river narrows. There, they were caught on a rock and attacked by hostile tribesmen who had been waiting in ambush. The odds against them were too high; the story goes that Park jumped into the river and it is assumed that he drowned. Amadi was taken prisoner.

In 1827, hopeful that his father might still be alive, Mungo Park's son, Thomas, set off to Africa in search of him. Within a month, however, all contact with him was lost. Stories circulated that he had died of fever but his body was never recovered. As recently as 2003, a man named Christian Velten set out on a six-month expedition following in the footsteps of Mungo Park. After a short time, contact with him was also lost.

Glossary

ambush (n) a surprise attack by people in a concealed place
be dogged by (v phr) to have problems/difficulties over a long period of time
rapids (n pl) a steep, rocky place in a river with a fast current

LISTENING

A PREDICT What logistical problems do you think 19th-century explorers faced? Think about:

- transportation
- communication
- provisions
- technology.

6.3 **B LISTEN FOR MAIN IDEA** Listen to the first part of a podcast about two Antarctic expeditions and answer the questions.

1 What were the names of the two explorers?

____

2 What was their goal?

____

3 When did these events take place?

____

4 What was the result of the expeditions?

____

6.4 **C** Listen to the rest of the recording. Check (✓) the topics mentioned.

- ☐ Communication
- ☐ Finances
- ☐ Friendship
- ☐ Food and nutrition
- ☐ Goals
- ☐ Historical background
- ☐ Mountaineering
- ☐ Route planning
- ☐ Transportation

6.5 **D LISTEN TO WRITE NOTES** Listen to the whole podcast. Write notes on the following questions.

1 Why Antarctica?	
2 What was life like for the explorers?	
3 What equipment was needed?	
4 How did Scott and Amundsen's goals differ?	
5 What means of transportation did Scott use?	
6 What was wrong with his choices?	
7 How did Amundsen plan his route?	
8 What was wrong with Scott's preparations?	

Glossary

depot (n) place where things are stored
hardship (n) situation in which life is very difficult
rations (n pl) restricted amounts of food for people such as soldiers

E REFLECT Does this story remind you of any other similar adventures you have read or heard about?

WRITING

A Look at the picture and the essay question below. How do you think the picture might be related to the content of this essay?

What are the benefits of discovering new species?

B Complete the essay by matching these missing topic sentences (1–5) to the paragraphs (a–e).

1 Penicillin was produced from a fungus.
2 If you thought there was nothing new under the sun, then think again.
3 Clearly, there is still much to learn about the surface of the planet we inhabit.
4 Each life form has a special role in the ecosystem.
5 'Biomimicry' is the science of copying nature's adaptations and applying them to technology.

The benefits of discovering NEW SPECIES

a ___ And new species may provide further breakthroughs in medicine. For example, extracts from a newly discovered plant, *Kindia gangan*, a member of the coffee family, suggest that it may have medical applications.

b ___ The gecko's ability to stick to walls and ceilings, the silk with which spiders spin their webs and the way butterfly wings react to light have all been exploited in technological innovations. Discoveries of new species may well lead to other innovations in the future.

c ___ Biologists estimate that the vast majority of life on Earth – between 3 and 100 million species – remains undiscovered. There are three enormous benefits to discovering new species: each new life form helps us understand more about biodiversity, may prove a valuable source of new medicines or could inspire new technology.

d ___ The benefits of continuing to discover new plants, insects and micro-organisms are enormous. They will help us treat the planet with greater knowledge and respect, with more informed conservation strategies. They can provide us with new medicines, possibly even for diseases we think incurable. Also, the weird and wonderful adaptations plants and creatures make to survive in their environments provide the inspiration for technologies that benefit us all.

e ___ Biodiversity is the way in which all these life forms function together to maintain a balance. As we discover new species, the better we understand how these systems work, which will help us implement more effective conservation strategies for threatened ecosystems such as coral reefs.

C STRUCTURING AN EXPOSITORY ESSAY Put the paragraphs (a–e) in the correct order (1–5).

1 introduction ___
2 first benefit ___
3 second benefit ___
4 third benefit ___
5 conclusion ___

WRITING PRACTICE

A PREPARE Read the essay question below. Use the questions 1–5 to write notes for the essay.

What are the benefits of foreign travel?

1 Have you ever traveled to another country? If not, would you like to?
2 What did/could you learn by visiting another country?
3 What did/could you learn about yourself?
4 Can traveling abroad teach you more about your own country?
5 Make a list of the benefits of travel.

B PLAN You are going to write an expository essay for the task in Exercise A.

- Organize your notes into an appropriate structure for an expository essay.
- Use a topic sentence to introduce each main paragraph.
- Finish with a conclusion that summarizes the points you made in the main body of the essay in the same order.

C WRITE Write your essay in 220–260 words.

GRAMMAR
it clefting

A Write one word in each blank to complete the sentences.

1 It ______ you who caused the problem; it was me.
2 It was the long ocean journey ______ put me off the idea.
3 The problem wasn't her lack of qualifications – ______ was her personality.
4 The money's OK, but ______ the hours that I don't like.
5 It was ______ visit my parents that I last went home.
6 It was my brother ______ persuaded me to go to college.
7 It was ______ I had to pay for something that I realized my wallet was missing.
8 It wasn't until we got home ______ we realized how close we had come to disaster.

B Rewrite the sentences using *it* clefting to draw attention to the underlined words or phrases.

1 I applied to run the race <u>to raise money for charity</u>.
______
2 <u>The physical challenge</u> isn't a problem for me; <u>the psychological challenge</u> is!
______
3 I've only noticed the pain in my legs <u>now</u>, <u>after I've been running for five days</u>.
______
4 <u>My sister</u> persuaded me to enter the race.
______
5 I didn't run <u>a marathon</u> – I ran <u>an ultramarathon</u>!
______

C Rewrite the sentences beginning with *It*. Sometimes more than one answer is possible.

1 They really wanted to see the landscape paintings.
______
2 He was to blame for breaking the window, not her.
______
3 The part Steven didn't understand was at the end.
______
4 I'm talking to you!
______
5 What bothers me is the cost.
______
6 Eliza said 'no' because she was scared.
______
7 You only really appreciate something when it's gone.
______
8 I didn't realize how dangerous it was until I got back.
______

D Complete the sentences so that they are true for you.

1 It wasn't only ______ it was ______.
2 It was my ______ who ______ me to ______.
3 It was because ______ that I ______.
4 It was to ______ that I ______ not to ______.

VOCABULARY
Feelings

A Chose the correct options to complete the text.

In touch with your FEELINGS?

A lot of the time, we do not have control over our emotions because they are instinctive reactions in response to a particular set of circumstances.

This is often useful – for example, when we are [1]***indifferent* / *disgusted*** by the sight of something, such as rotten food, it may well mean that we should stay away from it to be safe. Some people, however, sometimes try to stay in control of their emotions. They may want to appear tough or [2]***frustrated* / *resilient***. But sometimes these people can seem arrogant or [3]***superior* / *hysterical***.

However, there are times when we need to be a little [4]***humble* / *disgusted*** and accept that it is not always in our power to control how we feel. We should accept that it is natural to be [5]***devastated* / *humble*** when something awful happens.

But we should still strive to be [6]***grumpy* / *courageous*** even when we are frightened and to deal with things in a calm manner. At times like these, it really is possible to control our emotions.

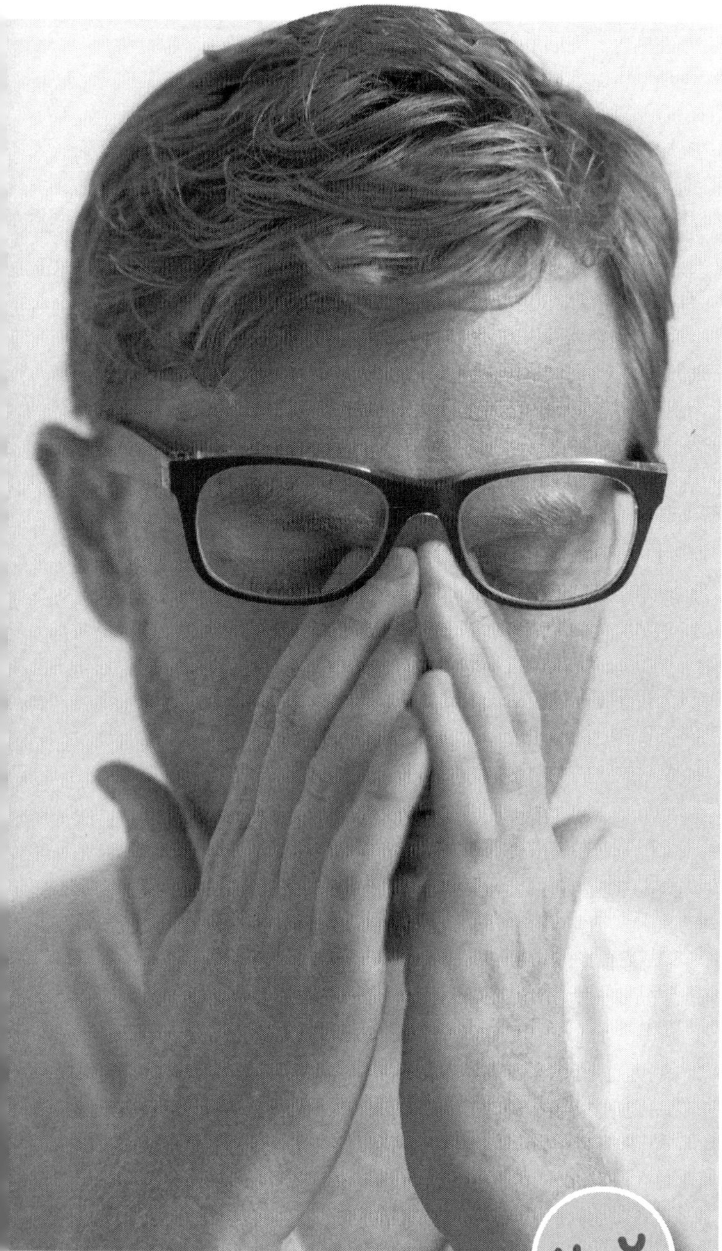

B **Complete the sentences with words from Exercise A. Sometimes more than one answer is possible.**

1 Jack was very ______________ and kept calm up until the last moment.

2 Emma is a very ______________ person who never likes to talk about her achievements.

3 When we saw the extent of the damage, we were ______________.

4 The BASE jumpers were left feeling ______________ after their jump was canceled three times due to high winds.

5 Carla seems almost ______________ to fear – however terrifying the situation, she always looks calm.

6 Nigel thinks he's better than everyone and he always acts in a(n) ______________ manner.

7 Stop being horrible to everyone! I think the reason you're so ______________ this morning is that you went to bed so late last night.

8 Alex was ______________ – he just kept screaming and crying.

PRONUNCIATION
Intonation in question tags

A **Look at the question tags and draw arrows to show whether they should have rising (↗) or falling (↘) intonation.**

1 It's ridiculous, isn't it? ___

2 Let's meet over the weekend, shall we? ___

3 We couldn't make it next weekend, could we? ___

4 Wow, that's good. You know what you're doing, don't you? ___

5 It's cold today, isn't it? ___

6 You couldn't help me out here, could you? ___

7.1 **B** **Listen to the sentences from Exercise A and check your answers.**

C **Practice saying the sentences in the same way as the speakers do in the recording in Exercise B.**

VOCABULARY
Polysemy; Intensifiers

A Complete the text with the words in the box.

application competition conditions land pressure sick

A life in CYBERCRIME

When I left school, my number one priority was to [1] ______ a well-paid job. I didn't care what. All I knew was that I was [2] ______ of studying and I wanted to use my computer skills.

I knew there was a lot of [3] ______ in the job market, especially for IT jobs – I had heard crazy numbers, like 500 people applying for one job. I felt a great deal of [4] ______ on me to get a job and the longer I stayed unemployed, the greater it became.

Almost a decade later and I am still amazed that I am now a legal computer hacker. That's right, I work for a security company and use my computer skills to make companies safer against cybercrime.

A very impressive [5] ______ got me my first interview with my current employer and after two more I was finally successful!

There were a few strange [6] ______ in the contract, and I have to be very cautious about personal data and intellectual property, but the money is very good.

B Rearrange the letters to make intensifiers.

1 Paul was **miymelnse** ______ proud of his success in the competition.
2 It's **tuetyrl** ______ ridiculous to expect your parents to support you when you're in your 20s.
3 I'm not **lgtoeharte** ______ sure I trust him.
4 Jane was **ayntcoiebl** ______ different after her trip to India.
5 It's **yetlairvel** ______ easy to get a job with that company – they're desperate for staff.
6 Georgia did **krrebmyaal** ______ well in her exams.
7 You can't call it 'his version of the truth'; it was an **utrogiht** ______ lie.
8 Things changed **ciradlyal** ______ once the new management team took over.
9 It's **capryalctil** ______ impossible to get a transfer to another branch – they almost never allow it.
10 Yeah, I think Philip was **tsohemwa** ______ confused – he had a strange look on his face!

GRAMMAR
what clefting and *all* clefting

A Find and correct the mistakes in the sentences.

1 What that happened was I got confused.

______

2 Why crashed the computer I have no idea!

______

3 Pets are easy – they all need is food, water and some attention.

______

4 That Lara likes about summer is being able to relax on the balcony.

______

5 You all need is a snack and some good company!

______

6 What's that Simon can't stand about this job – the silly rules!

______

7 That we ended up doing was taking the train.

______

8 I didn't have my phone on me so what did I do was ask a colleague to borrow hers.

______

B Rewrite the sentences using the words in parentheses.

1 In the end they turned back. (*what*)

______

2 We don't need anything except a map. (*all*)

______

3 I can't stand sleeping in a tent. (*what*)

______

4 Rex loves playing with his ball in the yard. (*what*)

______

5 They needed a drink of water. (*all*)

______

6 You need a vacation. (*what*)

______

7 Tanya wanted to be a ballerina more than anything. (*what*)

______

8 She's just asking for a short break. (*all*)

______

C Complete the second sentence so that it has a similar meaning to the first sentence. Write between two and five words, including the word given.

1 She loves basketball because she gets to meet up with her friends – that's what she loves most.

WHAT

______ basketball is that she gets to meet up with her friends.

2 She only wants a little bit of consideration, nothing else.

ALL

______ little bit of consideration, nothing else.

3 He didn't know what to do so he called his dad.

DID

He didn't know what to do so ______ his dad.

4 I like camping, except for the insects. I hate dealing with them.

STAND

______ camping is dealing with insects.

5 I've realized something about my job – it doesn't take a genius to do it!

WHAT

______ that it doesn't take a genius to do my job!

6 My sister doesn't remember much about her first school – just playing outside.

ALL

______ about her first school is playing outside.

PRONUNCIATION
any and *really*

A Underline *really* and *any* in these sentences when they are stressed.

1 The movie was really amazing, actually – we loved it!

2 I don't want any old doctor – I want the one I always see.

3 The questions they asked me were really ridiculous!

4 Any questions you have will be answered at the end, OK?

5 Well, you don't tell your password to just anybody.

6 Let's go – anywhere's better than here!

7 The test was really hard but he thinks he passed.

8 'Which movie do you want to watch?'
'Oh, any one. You choose.'

7.2 **B Listen to the sentences from Exercise A.**

C Practice saying the sentences in the same way as the speakers do in the recording.

READING

A PREDICT Look at the picture and think about these questions.

1 What are some of the dangers involved in surfing?
2 What is it about this sport that appeals to people?

B READ FOR GIST Read *Surf's up* and answer the questions.

1 What is the main danger for surfers?
2 What claim do surfers make about the appeal of their sport?
3 What impression do non-surfers have of the surfing life?
4 As a profession, does surfing pay well?

C Complete the article with the reference devices in the box.

it	it's	many	one	such incidents	that (x2)	those who	which	you

D READ FOR REFERENCES What do the reference devices in Exercise C refer to? Decide if they are anaphoric: referring back (A), cataphoric: referring forward (C) or exophoric: referring outside the text (E).

1 ___ 3 ___ 5 ___ 7 ___ 9 ___
2 ___ 4 ___ 6 ___ 8 ___ 10 ___

Glossary

endorsement (n) support given by a well-known person to products as a form of advertising
riptide (n) a strong surface current from the shore out to sea
sponsorship (n) support from an organization that promotes sporting or artistic activity
trajectory (n) path, direction of a moving object

E REFLECT Think about the answers to these questions.

1 Why do we sometimes like to be scared?
2 Would you like to earn your living from doing an extreme sport? Why/Why not?

Surf's up

[1] ______ may look like fun in the sun, but for some surfing is a job, a full-time occupation. Also a passion. And there is money to be made – if you're good enough. I'll come back to that later. But before [2] ______ get on your board, and paddle out to where the waves break, you should be aware of some of the dangers involved in surfing – or just being in the ocean.

Shark attacks are everyone's fear, surfer or not, but they are not as frequent a cause of injury or death as other factors; though [3] ______ do get a lot of media coverage. Waves are powerful forces of nature and a wipeout, or being thrown off your board, can cause serious injuries. Your board, too, becomes a danger in such incidents, as it is sent spinning into the air and you have no idea where it will land. You just hope it doesn't hit you, especially with the pointy end. Now you're struggling in rough water, there are riptides to worry about, which are usually present at good surfing areas. [4] ______ takes us to the most obvious danger – drowning. So why take it up, let alone make it your profession?

The excitement, of course. Even with a small wave, say one meter high, you experience the awesome power of nature – and you're going with it. Riding [5] ______ taller than yourself, the experience is even greater. [6] ______ claim there's no better sensual experience in the world. There's nothing but the wave, your board and your body – all your senses fully engaged: the sound of the surf, the taste of salt, the colors and the sensation of speed. The slightest shift in weight will alter your trajectory in the direction you want to go, or send you crashing into the surf. And no two waves are ever the same. An extreme challenge, then, but one that brings great pleasure. Imagine what it would be like to catch a wave as tall as a tower. For some, [7] ______ is their speciality; but I assume they must be inhumanly confident or mad!

For [8] ______ are just onlookers, the lifestyle, too, has its attractions. What could be better than a job that takes you all over the world to exotic places, spending your days on beaches? It sounds like a permanent vacation. But [9] ______ not all travel and parties. Like anything worth doing, it takes hard work, ambition and time. I mentioned earlier that there was money to be made, but it's not great. There's no real job security, like a salary, health insurance, pension or paid leave. Top surfers get money from winning competitions, and a lot of that goes toward traveling to the next competition. It's a sport and like, say, tennis, those at the top get the big money, while the rest fight it out for smaller and smaller amounts. Apart from [10] ______, once a surfer has made a name for himself or herself, there's money to be made from sponsorships and endorsements.

LISTENING

A PREDICT What personal qualities do you think a performer would need to be a successful tightrope walker?

7.3 **B LISTEN FOR SPECIFIC INFORMATION** Listen to a program about tightrope walking. Complete the texts with a word or short phrase in each blank.

Nik Wallenda

The famous tightrope walker comes from a family of [1] ______________ performers going back generations. His great-grandfather died in [2] ______________ trying to walk between two buildings. His most famous stunt, walking across the Niagara Falls, attracted [3] ______________ viewers.

Philippe Petit

A [4] ______________ movie about his achievement called *Man on Wire* was released in 2008. He found fame after walking a tightrope between two skyscrapers in [5] ______________ City for a distance of [6] ______________ meters. The event was organized [7] ______________ because it was illegal. A [8] ______________ were used to fire a guiding rope across the space.

7.3 **C LISTEN FOR CAUSATION** Listen again and choose the correct options (a, b or c) to answer the questions or complete the sentences.

1 What is the key factor behind Nik Wallenda's successful career as a tightrope walker?
   a Pressure from his family
   b The achievements of his great-grandfather
   c His desire for publicity

2 He attracts audiences of millions because
   a he walked across the Niagara Falls.
   b they think he has a lot of charisma.
   c he knows how to successfully exploit the media.

3 Many people became interested in Philippe Petit again because
   a his exploits are illegal.
   b his most famous walk involved New York's Twin Towers.
   c of a movie which featured his most famous achievement.

4 What was the immediate result of Philippe Petit's walk between the Twin Towers?
   a The New York police arrested him.
   b He became famous overnight.
   c A movie was made about his exploits.

Glossary

feat (n) an impressive and often dangerous act
heist (n) an organized robbery (of a bank, jewelry store, etc)

D REFLECT Think about the answers to these questions.

1 Do you think that the people you heard about in the recording are courageous or foolish?
2 Why do people enjoy watching such terrifying stunts?

Tree Surgeon – Montana

The US Forest Service is recruiting an arborist/ tree surgeon. The job involves collecting data, assessing tree health and treatment, assessing hazards posed by trees, pruning and removing branches and planting and felling trees.

A certificate in Forest Management is not essential, but some experience in woodland ecology and conservation or arboriculture would be valuable. We are looking for an experienced climber skilled in the use and maintenance of power tools. The candidate must be prepared to work outdoors in all conditions, be able to work at heights, remain calm in tense situations, follow instructions in detail and work well as a member of a team.

Applications to: Henry Swaffer, US Forest Service.

Dear Mr. Swaffer,

I am writing to apply for the position of tree surgeon at the US Forest Service.

You will see on my résumé (attached) that I have a certificate in arboriculture and experience in woodland conservation as a volunteer for the American Forest Foundation, where I [1]was in charge of a team [2]whose task was to collect data about the health and growth of trees. This work provided me with valuable insights into woodland preservation.

Later, I [3]became the manager of a small tree surgery company where I [4]had responsibility for the care and maintenance of woodland in the Bozeman area on behalf of the local council. Here my climbing skills and expertise in the use of power tools were put to good use. [5]I was also involved in the development of new methods of tree preservation, which the council subsequently adopted as policy. The job also allowed me to demonstrate my leadership qualities and ability to work with a team.

I look forward to the opportunity of an interview.

Best regards,

Anthony Waite

WRITING

A Look at the picture to the left. What skills, personal qualities and certifications do you think are required to do this job?

B Read the job advertisement and answer the questions.

1 Which of the skills, qualities and certifications that you wrote down in Exercise A are mentioned?

2 Which are the most important for the job?

C **USING POWER VERBS** Read the cover letter. Rewrite the underlined sections using verbs to make the letter more powerful.

WRITING PRACTICE

A **PREPARE** Read the job advertisement and underline the key information regarding skills and certifications required.

Lifeguard – Team Leader at Ocean Resorts

We are looking for a dynamic individual to join our team at Ocean Resorts. Your role will be to support, coach and guide team members in creating a safe and fun environment.

The candidate will have proven experience in busy ocean and poolside environments and have a current American Red Cross Lifeguarding certification. Excellent physical fitness is essential, as well as being a strong swimmer.

A practical knowledge of first aid and a commitment to health and safety are also required. Flexibility in the role and the ability to take on extra responsibilities when required is a plus.

Applications to: Mr. Kevin Scholes, Manager, Ocean Resorts.

B **PLAN** You are going to write a cover letter in response to the ad for a lifeguard.

- Use the information you underlined in Exercise A.
- Organize your notes into an appropriate form for a cover letter.
- Use power verbs to talk about your achievements.

C **WRITE** Write your letter in 120–200 words.

VOCABULARY
Health problems

A Complete the text below with the words in the box.

dislocate	fractured	pressure	pulled
rash	rate	sore	sprained

B The words in bold are in the wrong sentence. Replace with the correct word.

1 Geoff's leg's in plaster because he **inflamed** ________ it when he slipped on some ice.

2 I didn't warm up properly before the match and I **sore** ________ a muscle.

3 My knee is very **fractured** ________ – it has swelled up a lot so I'm putting ice on it.

4 A normal resting heart **blood** ________ is 60 to 100 beats per minute.

5 If I fall asleep in a chair, I usually wake up with a **sprained** ________ back.

6 Kate's **pulled** ________ her ankle – she twisted it on the stairs but it's not too serious.

7 I have a **rate** ________ on my skin and I don't know what's causing it.

8 The first thing the doctor did was to take my **rash** ________ pressure.

HEALTH CHAT

Post your questions or medical issue on the HealthChat Portal and a qualified doctor will respond within minutes. You can post in both the private and public chat forums.

Woke up with a [1] ________ throat a few days ago, and a strange itchy red [2] ________ on my arms, chest and legs. Am seeing the doctor tomorrow …

Jared | 3:44 pm

Went for a ride last Saturday and noticed that my heart [3] ________ was much faster than usual. Got it checked out and found I have high blood [4] ________. My doctor thinks it might be stress-related.

Emily | 3:45 pm

Came off my mountain bike – again! – and [5] ________ my ankle. It was extremely painful, but could have been worse. The race medical team bandaged it up for me. Really glad it wasn't [6] ________ or broken!

Connor | 3:45 pm

Having [7] ________ a muscle in my leg about a month ago, I thought I was getting fit again – only to [8] ________ my shoulder this weekend. Really painful! And spent four hours in A&E!

Liz | 3:47 pm

GRAMMAR
Adjective clauses with complex relative pronouns

A **Complete the sentences with one preposition in each blank.**

1 The police were interested in interviewing victims ________ whose houses the burglars had broken.

2 The treadmill ________ which I was most interested is no longer for sale.

3 The brochure lists all the surfaces that the device can be attached ________.

4 He was very formal on the phone and said, '________ whom am I speaking?'

5 The thief stole a car, ________ which he made his getaway.

6 'I don't know who this package is for.' 'Well, who is it addressed ________?'

7 It's a wellness treatment ________ which I've read a lot recently.

8 There are six team members, ________ whom three are women.

B **Rewrite the sentences using the word in parentheses.**

1 This is the person. Her fitness business is now worth millions. (*whose*)
This is ________.

2 I trust Jonah. I trust him more than anyone. (*person*)
Jonah is ________.

3 I need a strategy which makes it impossible for me to get a virus. (*whereby*)
I need a strategy ________.

4 Be careful you don't get a training injury. You might never recover from it. (*from*)
Be careful you don't get ________.

5 We are targeting people. Exercise is not a priority for them. (*whom*)
We are targeting ________.

6 The owner of the company is very satisfied. The profits all go into his pockets. (*into*)
The owner of the company, ________.

PRONUNCIATION
Building suspense

A **Read the sentences aloud. Use intonation and pauses to build suspense.**

1 My health app told me that yesterday I did 5,000 steps!

2 Well, someone in this room has just passed their exams!

3 There's no more waiting – you get the results at the touch of a button.

4 I spent an hour shopping for spices and after all that, I didn't find the one I wanted.

5 It hasn't really sunk in yet but … I won first prize!

6 Do you want to hear the good news? Danny's getting out of the hospital … tomorrow!

8.1 **B** **Listen to the sentences from Exercise A.**

C **Practice saying the sentences in the same way as the speakers do in Exercise B.**

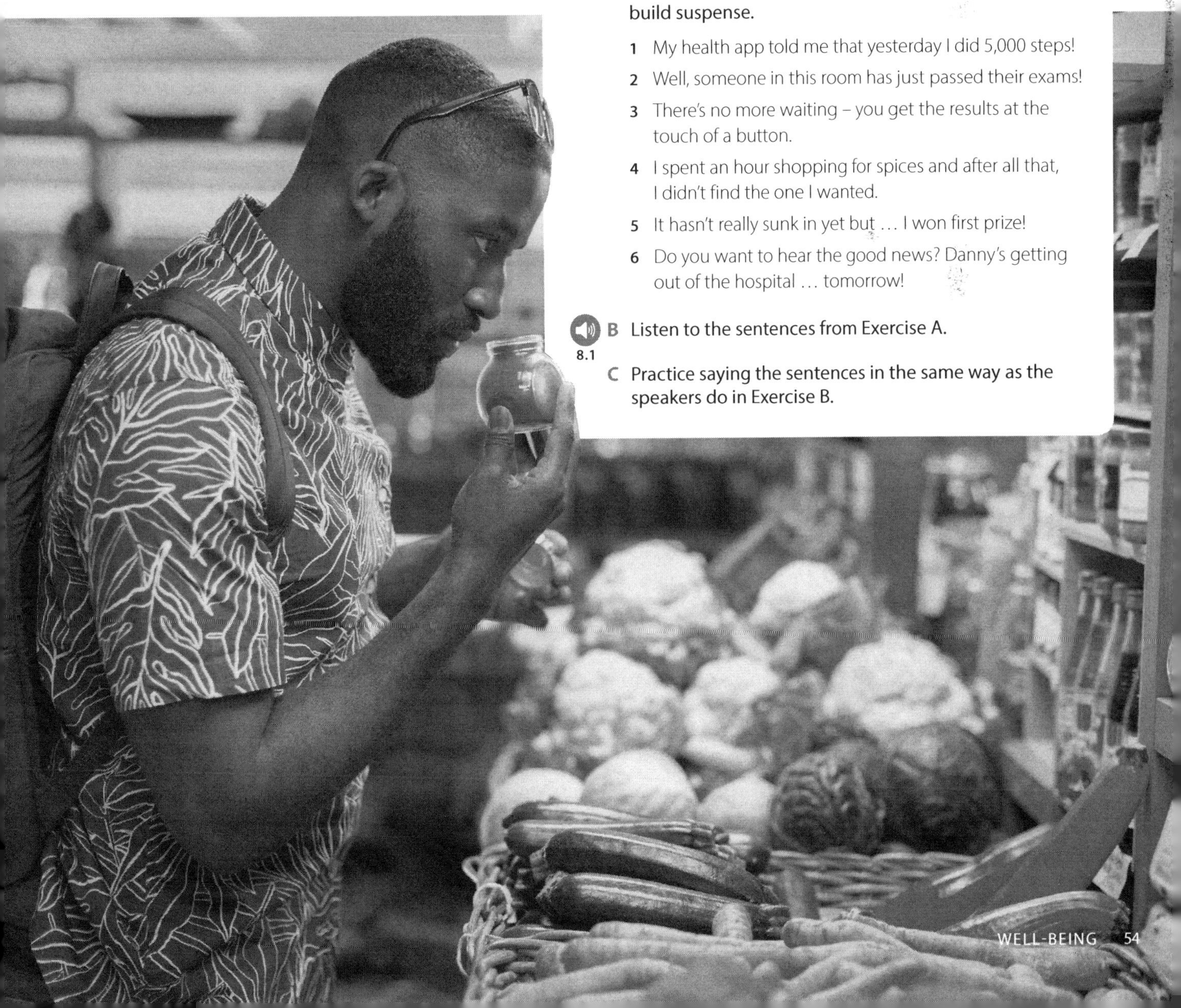

VOCABULARY
Idioms; Describing taste

A Choose the correct options to complete the text.

A TOUGH GAME

Only once had Roberto taken part in any kind of sporting competition, and that was in a tennis match. Someone persuaded him to play but his [1]***cup of tea / gut feeling*** was that he was making a terrible mistake!

A bigger mistake was watching his opponent play in a match before. That certainly [2]***made a meal of it / gave him food for thought*** because Roberto could see how good he was. Roberto very nearly [3]***got cold feet / kept an eye out***, but he decided to [4]***give it his best shot / take it with a pinch of salt***.

His opponent was very good and Roberto was clearly [5]***out of his depth / head and shoulders below him***. Roberto thought about [6]***moving the goalposts / throwing in the towel***, but he stuck at it. In the end, Roberto lost of course, but he likes to think he put up a good fight!

B Complete the sentences with one word to describe taste in each blank. The first letter is given to help you.

1 I don't like **f**__________ drinks like lemonade or soda.
2 **C**__________ vegetables like carrots, which you can really bite into, are a good substitute for chips.
3 I think the milk's gone **s**__________. Don't drink it.
4 Carol loves spicy food, but Mark prefers his to be **m**__________.
5 Jeanette always makes her food look really **a**__________.
6 Susan made a lovely smooth **c**__________ sauce to go with the mushrooms.
7 I like the **t**__________, slightly **a**__________ taste of grapefruit.
8 It's a terrible place. The meals they serve there are always **b**__________ and taste of nothing.
9 Their chips are usually covered in vinegar – far too **s**__________ for my taste.

PRONUNCIATION
Pronunciation of idioms

A Circle the words in the underlined idioms which are stressed. Then practice saying the sentences.

1 No, tennis <u>isn't really my cup of tea</u>.
2 I know it was a penalty, but he really <u>made a meal of it</u>, rolling all over the field like that!
3 Murphy didn't take part in the robbery – he was only there to <u>keep an eye out</u> for the police.
4 He exaggerates a lot, so you can take most of what he says <u>with a grain of salt</u>.
5 Eva was the best student in our class – she was <u>head and shoulders above</u> the rest of us.
6 We knew where we were at the beginning of this project, but if the boss keeps <u>moving the goalposts</u>, we'll never get anywhere.

8.2 **B Listen to the sentences from Exercise A.**

C Practice saying the sentences in the same way as the speakers do in Exercise B.

GRAMMAR
Pronouns and determiners

A Choose the correct options to complete the sentences.

1 It would be better for all of us if we did *any* / *more* exercise.
2 There was a choice of two desserts, but I didn't want *either* / *neither*.
3 *Most people* / *The most people* feel better when they are active.
4 Do you want some coffee? I'll make you *some* / *some coffee.*
5 Some people like team sports, but *others people* / *others* prefer individual activities.
6 There were *a few* / *very few* members there, so they postponed the meeting until the following week.
7 One *of* / *from* the fitness programs is bound to interest you.
8 There's *a little* / *little* point in worrying about it – we can't change anything now.

B Find and correct the mistakes in the sentences.

1 When you're doing a serious hike, you can't drink too much of water – in fact, most people don't drink enough.

______

2 There were two vegan options, but I didn't like or want both of them.

______

3 They who followed the diet reported an average loss of three kilos in the first week.

______

4 You have too much sugar and salt in your diet – it's best if you cut back on neither.

______

5 There are only few restaurants that serve good vegetarian food in this city.

______

6 You drink a lot of coffee, and I think you'd sleep better if you drank less of.

______

7 These are your books – my are still over there where I left them.

______

8 Jamie only needs six hours of sleep a night, but I can never seem to get enough of.

______

a

b

FOOD, GLORIOUS FOOD

We are what we eat? Well I'm not sure what this received wisdom means if you're on a charcoal diet! With so much advice about food and eating available to us today, it can be hard to know what is good information and what can be downright harmful. With a growing global wellness industry eager to package and push us a never-ending stream of diets and food products, we decided to take a closer look at some of the diets out there currently.

Charcoal

Black cheese or black ice cream, anyone? Almost any foodstuff can be made black by adding activated charcoal. The thinking behind this is that charcoal is a porous form of carbon which supposedly absorbs harmful bacteria in the digestive system. While this may be true, critics of the diet argue that activated charcoal is so greedy it absorbs anything in your stomach, even the good stuff like food, vitamins and the medicines you might be taking. Not surprisingly, the fans of this diet don't accept this. I don't know about you, but, for me, variety of color is a major 'ingredient' in the enjoyment of food. So that's one thing that would make it harder for me to follow this diet.

Ketogenic

Sounds rather scientific, doesn't it? The keto diet, as it is called, allegedly turns your body into a fat-burning machine by avoiding carbohydrates such as pasta. Admittedly, those who have tried it swear that it works and have lost weight and benefited from improved health associated with weight loss. Like most diets, though, this one also has its critics, who argue that any diet that excludes an entire food group from its regimen is bound to have some side-effects, or not provide all the nutrition we need. But if losing weight is your goal, you could give it a try.

Cauliflower

Not just cauliflower, but cabbage, or any diet that claims sticking to any one foodstuff will bring rapid and amazing results. Cauliflower, it seems, can replace bread as a principal foodstuff! You can even get cauliflower pizza crust! There's no doubt that cauliflower is good for you; it is rich in anti-oxidants, is anti-inflammatory, is full of vitamin C and other vitamins and helps with digestion. It is also thought to improve both heart and brain health. But some dieticians and nutritionists advise that it should just be a part, along with other vegetables, of a well-balanced diet.

Vegan

Veganism seems to be very popular right now. Strict vegans will have nothing to do with any foodstuff that comes from animals. As well as meat and fish, they reject basic everyday foods such as milk, butter, eggs, even honey. Interestingly some vegans claim to enjoy better physical and mental health as a result – but critics might respond: well, they would, wouldn't they? Not all vegans do it for health reasons. They adopt veganism as a way of life, believing that modern farming methods are cruel to animals and harmful to the environment. It is an ethical diet, but opinions vary as to how filling or satisfying vegan meals are – gastronomically, that is.

READING

A SKIM Read *Food, glorious food* quickly. Match the diet plans to the pictures (a–d).

B READ FOR DETAIL Read the article again and answer the questions.

1. Which diet is said to be good for weight loss?
2. Which diet is said to be a larger lifestyle choice?
3. Which diet might have a negative effect on digestion?

C READ TO IDENTIFY OPINIONS Read the article again. Underline examples of the following.

1. Adverbs to show a positive attitude
2. Adverbs to show a negative attitude
3. Attitude to reported information
4. Use of colloquial asides, tag questions and rhetorical questions to comment on information

Glossary

gastronomist (n) person who studies the art of eating well
porous (adj) having a lot of very small holes so that air or water can pass through

D REFLECT Are any of the diets popular in your country?

c

d

LISTENING

A PREDICT You are going to listen to a radio interview about astronauts and well-being. What do you think might be some of the challenges of this kind of work?

8.3 **B LISTEN FOR GIST** Listen to the interview. Some parts are somewhat hard to hear because of interference on the line. Were any of your ideas from Exercise A mentioned?

8.3 **C LISTEN WITH NOISE** Listen to the interview again and choose the correct options (a or b).

1 Angela Schneider specializes in
  a research into weight loss and healthy eating.
  b nutrition and diet for astronauts.

2 What does Angela say about iron in the blood of a space traveler?
  a There's too much.
  b There's too little.

3 Astronauts are more likely
  a to break their bones when they come back.
  b to follow a strength training program.

4 According to Angela, the food which astronauts eat today is
  a delicious.
  b unappetizing.

8.3 **D LISTEN FOR DETAIL** Listen again. Write notes on what you hear in the table below.

1 **Key elements of an astronaut's diet**	
2 **Injuries that an astronaut could suffer after returning to Earth**	
3 **Measures to prevent injuries**	
4 **Amount of iron in an astronaut's blood**	
5 **Food items which appear on the menu**	

Glossary

collaborative (adj) involving people or groups working together
palatable (adj) tasting good enough to eat
supplement (n) a special food that you add to your regular diet

E REFLECT Think about the answers to these questions.

1 How important do you think space travel is for the future of the human race?

2 Would you change your diet for work?

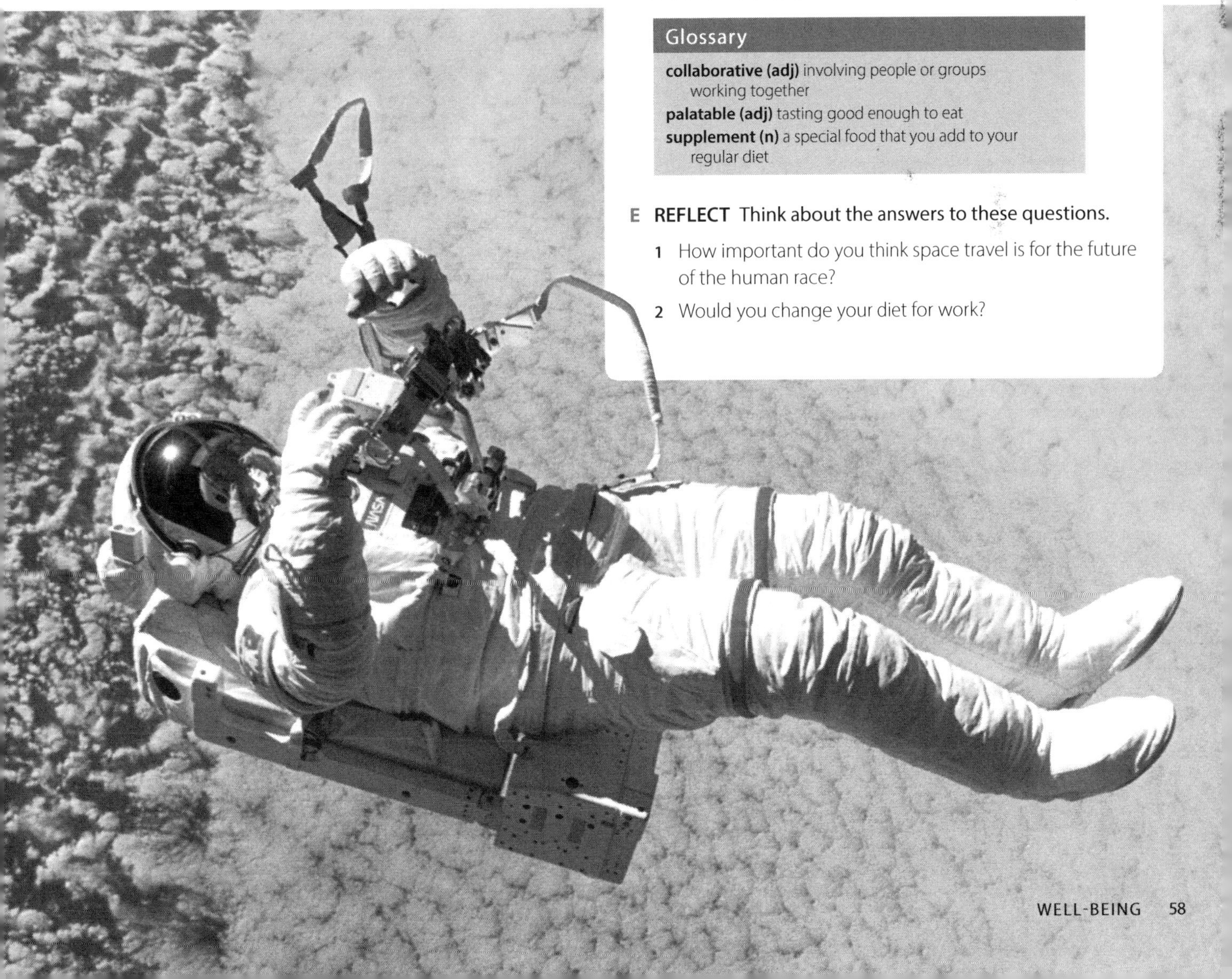

WRITING

A What physical and psychological effects might 'overtraining' have on an athlete?

B Read the first paragraph of *Time to slow down?* and complete the tasks.

1 Underline the keywords.

2 Which is the best one-sentence summary of the paragraph (a, b or c)? Give reasons for your choice.

a Consult a doctor before undertaking a training program and devise your own programs to avoid overtraining.

b Overtraining syndrome is the result of training too much and typically leads to both physical and psychological symptoms.

c Too much training can push the body beyond its capacity to recover and both physiological and psychological symptoms may present themselves.

C PARAPHRASING Now read the second paragraph of the article and complete the tasks.

1 Underline the keywords and ideas.

2 What is the main focus of this paragraph?

3 Write a one- or two-sentence summary of this paragraph.

D Read the rest of the article and note down keywords and ideas.

WRITING PRACTICE

A PREPARE Read *Time to slow down?* again. Think about the answers to these questions and write notes.

1 What are the main points of each paragraph?

2 Which words (proper nouns, technical vocabulary) can you reuse in your summary?

3 Which parts of the text are unnecessary for your summary?

B PLAN You are going to write a summary of *Time to slow down*?

- Organize your notes from Writing Exercises B–D.
- Use your own words as much as possible. Check that you have not repeated unnecessary phrases or structures from the article.
- Make sure you have included all the key points.

C WRITE Write your summary in approximately 60 words.

TIME TO SLOW DOWN?

Consistency in strength, mobility and cardiovascular training is often held up as a key determiner for success and receiving the full health benefits of these types of exercise. But sometimes there is a fine line between consistency and what is known as 'overtraining syndrome'. Put simply, too much training can force the body beyond its capacity to recover. Those that push themselves hard in sports professionally or recreationally may be especially at risk. According to research by the *Journal of Athletic Training*, both physiological and psychological symptoms may present themselves when overtraining occurs.

Physiological symptoms

Various physical symptoms of overtraining include unexplained muscle and weight loss, an inability to build muscle among male athletes and excessive thirst. The cardiovascular system can be affected, with increased heart rate and a greater length of time to return to a normal heart rate, and both increased and decreased levels of blood pressure. Another common indicator is injury, which may occur as a result of the kind of loads used in training or because the body is unable to recover from training. Furthermore, there may be an increased risk of infections such as colds.

Psychological symptoms

It is not necessarily as easy to determine overtraining from psychological symptoms but if, for example, athletes find themselves generally run-down or mentally unprepared for training, this may be a warning sign. Sleep disturbance, tiredness and loss of energy all suggest potential overtraining. Emotional mood may also provide a clue, as mood swings and feelings of irritability and anger have been commonly observed. The self-confidence of an athlete may also decrease while levels of cortisol (stress hormones) might rise. Finally, it's sensible to keep an eye on the regularity of meals as loss of appetite has been noted as a symptom.

Prevention and treatment

The advice of medical professionals should be sought in cases of overtraining. Trainers and coaches also have a particularly important role to play in monitoring athletes for symptoms, as well as devising training programs that prevent injury. Beyond recognizing symptoms, action must be taken to tackle them, for example, through periods of rest or decreases in training intensity. It is possible to address psychological symptoms as well, by modifying programs and sometimes allowing athletes more autonomy in the design of a program.

VOCABULARY
Slang

A Choose the correct options to complete the sentences.

1 Mark was *awesome* / *stoked* / *bummed* when he got a place at the college he wanted to go to.

2 Jack's always *whining* / *hanging out* / *chilling out* about not having any money, but he doesn't go out and look for a job!

3 In the UK, people refer informally to a male stranger as a *buddy* / *guy* / *bloke*, but in the US, he might be called a *buck* / *dude* / *grand*.

4 $100 for a laptop? That sounds like a *shady* / *crash* / *beat* deal to me – are you sure it's not *excellent* / *taken care of* / *stolen*?

5 They offered to buy me a *TV* / *shambles* / *grand*, but I was *cos* / *do* / *like*, what do I want that for? I need some *crash* / *wheels* / *bucks* so I can get around!

B Read the extract from a story. Replace the words and phrases in italics with slang expressions from the box.

broke   bucks   could do with   crashed   grand   in good shape   set her back   shambles

1 ______ 5 ______
2 ______ 6 ______
3 ______ 7 ______
4 ______ 8 ______

Rose Robinson woke up and took a look around her apartment. It was a [1]*mess*. She'd come home at who knows what time and [2]*fallen asleep* on the couch.

She knew she [3]*would benefit from* finding a new place, but she also knew that it would [4]*cost* at least a [5]*thousand dollars* and she just didn't have that kind of money.

She looked in her pocket, 'Seven [6]*dollars*! I'm sick and tired of being [7]*without money*,' she muttered to herself, 'I need some money fast and then I'll be [8]*fine*!' Just then, a dangerous and life-changing plan started to form in her sleepy brain.

PRONUNCIATION
Pronouncing vague expressions

A Underline the vague expressions in the sentences. How would you pronounce them?

1 I feel kind of strange – like I've been here before or something.

2 We have to give a talk, or a speech, or something like that.

3 I have to do some jobs – shopping, cleaning and so on.

4 You know, I think that, in some way or another, he must be involved.

5 So, in a sense, this is the easiest job in the world!

6 What do you take me for – some sort of fool?

7 Don't give me excuses like you overslept or whatever.

8 My course covers health and safety issues, stuff like that.

B Listen to the sentences from Exercise A. 9.1

C Practice saying the sentences in the same way as the speakers do in Exercise B.

GRAMMAR
Noun phrases

A Underline two noun phrases in each sentence.

1 Those students who haven't completed the assignment should stay behind at the end of the lecture.
2 Both of the solutions he suggested sounded a little like a desperate attempt to please the boss.
3 He invested all the money he'd saved up into some crazy get-rich-quick scheme and lost everything.
4 The thing that annoys Pierre most is the way young people don't seem to care about language.
5 Three of the 20 people present were first-time attendees.
6 The idea that simply punishing children teaches them to behave has fallen out of favor with many modern educationalists.
7 Do you know a good place to eat that would suit a group of hungry teenagers?
8 Sometimes it seems to me that almost everyone I know is hooked on some computer game or other.

B Find and correct the mistakes in the sentences.

1 I spend all my free time almost doing sports.

______

2 The belief what you can change things is all you need in order to make a difference.

______

3 The person where I spoke to didn't seem to have a clue what was happening.

______

4 I need a place for staying for a few days.

______

5 Both of ideas seem a little hard to put into practice.

______

6 The woman who sitting next to Claire is Frances.

______

7 Very few of people in this country have traveled abroad.

______

8 The interviewer was impressed by the fact how I knew so much about their company.

______

C Complete each sentence with one word only.

1 Unfortunately ______ of the students failed yesterday's history exam – only a few passed.
2 ______ man sitting at the bus stop works in a science laboratory.
3 Out of all my colleagues, Daniel is the ______ I trust the most.
4 Few members ______ the community spoke out against the mayor.
5 Unlike ours, ______ study was well funded, so they could afford the best equipment.
6 The fact ______ I love communication affected my decision to study languages.

PRONUNCIATION
Intrusive stops

A Read the sentences aloud, paying attention to the way you pronounce the underlined sections.

1. A lot of youngsters enjoy going out to dance.
2. Hamsters build nests for warmth.
3. It must be nice being a prince, but your life would be pretty intense.
4. I did four lengths of the pool, but I didn't have the strength to do more.
5. Once you get into trouble for something, it can influence the way other people see you.

9.2 **B** Listen to the sentences from Exercise A.

C Practice saying the sentences in the same way as the speakers do in Exercise B.

VOCABULARY
Verb + object + base form; Gestures and body language

A Match the beginnings of the sentences (1–8) to the endings (a–h).

1. Listen! I think I can hear someone ____
2. A thoughtful family friend let me ____
3. The manager had us ____
4. I heard a dog ____
5. Not only must justice be done, but it must also be seen ____
6. I wonder if you could help me ____
7. I thought I could feel something ____
8. Were you made ____

a climbing up my leg.
b bark once, and then there was silence.
c coming. Don't make a sound.
d fill in this form. It looks difficult.
e to sign any documents when you started working there?
f drive her car to see if it suited me.
g to be done.
h wait for an hour before she spoke to us.

B Choose the correct options to complete the story.

When John caught up with Sharon, she was sitting on a rock, 1***gazing / crossing / bending*** out to sea. She held something in her hand that she was 2***folding / fidgeting / shaking*** with.

'Are you OK?' John said gently. She just 3***shrugged / smirked / grinned*** her shoulders.

Then she 4***glared / nodded / shook*** her head and said, 'No, I'm not OK!'

'Sharon, what's wrong?' John asked. She turned to look at him and 5***winked / blinked / wiggled*** her eyes a few times as the bright sun lit up her face.

She took the ring off her finger, stood up and 6***beckoned / stared / leaned*** him to follow her to the water's edge. She 7***bent / pointed / folded*** back across the beach and said 'That was where we met'. She threw the ring into the ocean.

John 8***grinned / crossed / raised*** his eyebrows and stood open-mouthed, too shocked to react.

GRAMMAR
Participle clauses and verbless clauses

A Complete the second sentence so that it has a similar meaning to the first sentence. Write between two and five words, including the word given.

1 Because she got out of bed early, Nina had the view of the city all to herself.
UP
________________, Nina had the view of the city all to herself.

2 I didn't know anything about math, but I still worked out the answer.
DESPITE
________________ anything about math, I still worked out the answer.

3 If you do the job properly, it shouldn't take more than a day.
DONE
________________ shouldn't take more than a day.

4 As I am not practical, it made more sense after I had read the instructions.
READING
________________ instructions meant it made more sense.

5 He was not interested in any special offers because he had bought a new phone yesterday.
JUST
________________ phone yesterday, he was not interested in any special offers.

6 If you give them a positive environment, most children will learn quickly and easily.
RIGHT
________________ environment, most children will learn quickly and easily.

B Find and correct the mistakes with participle and verbless clauses.

1 They were feeling threatened, the animals instinctively hid behind the wall.
____

2 Had never been on a plane before, I was both excited and nervous.
____

3 If you successful in your application, you will be notified by email.
____

4 Grown up in the US, Marvin has always spoken English well.
____

5 Been exhausted and short on money, Carrie cut short her trip to Bolivia.
____

6 Before started work in insurance, Lionel was a factory worker.
____

7 Despite I hadn't been there before, I soon found my way around.
____

8 While suffering badly from the flu, a couple of close friends visited Angela every day.
____

C Choose the correct options (a, b or c) to complete the text.

Languages contain so much of a people's culture that it's a shame that more isn't done to preserve them. [1]________________, I find languages infinitely fascinating. I thought I might be able to help preserve African languages, [2]________________ much of my youth there.

Many of these languages, [3]________________ by just a handful of people, are dying. [4]________________ in funds to preserve them themselves, many tribes are destined to lose a valuable part of their heritage. So I applied to work with an association whose mission is to preserve the culture of several African tribes.

[5]________________ the head of the association, I felt inspired to get to work. However, we must frequently rely on the elders of a community, who, [6]________________ how to read or write, struggle with transcribing words and phrases. This presents further challenges with accurate translation.

1 **a** A linguist **b** Being a linguist **c** To be a linguist
2 **a** while to spend **b** spent **c** having spent
3 **a** having spoken **b** speaking **c** spoken
4 **a** Lacked **b** Lacking **c** Being lacking
5 **a** After meeting **b** Being met **c** Despite meeting
6 **a** never teaching **b** having never been taught **c** having never taught

WORDS *have* POWER

In a well-documented experiment (Bargh, Chen and Burrows, 1996), students at New York University were given five words which they had to use in order to construct sentences of four words (i.e. they had to leave one word out). They did this 30 times. Of the 30 groups of words, 15 contained words related in some way either to rudeness (e.g. *disturb* or *annoyingly*) or politeness (e.g. *respect* or *patiently*). There was also a neutral set, containing words that were neither connected to rudeness nor politeness (e.g. *give* or *occasionally*). Students didn't know whether they had the 'rude set', the 'polite set' or the 'neutral set'. In fact, they thought the experiment was simply to test their speed in forming grammatically correct sentences.

Participants were told to come and find the experimenter when they were finished. What they didn't realize was that this was really the important part of the experiment, because the researchers had staged a delay, whereby the student was forced to wait while the experimenter was deeply involved in a conversation with another 'participant' (in reality, another researcher). Unknown to the student, a stopwatch had been activated the moment they stood up from the task with the sentences. The purpose of the experiment was to see how long the students would wait before interrupting.

READING

A PREDICT Do you think that words or names have the power to change people's behavior? How?

B READ FOR GIST Read *Words have power* quickly. Were any of your ideas in Exercise A mentioned? Have you changed your opinion? Why/Why not?

C READ FOR DETAIL Read the article again. Are these sentences true (T) or false (F)? Correct the sentences that are false.

1. Students were asked to make 30 sentences of 4 words each. *T / F*
2. The experiment was to see how fast they could form sentences. *T / F*
3. Participants were timed to see how quickly they completed the task. *T / F*
4. Most of the participants waited ten minutes after the task. *T / F*
5. The last paragraph suggests that we purposely avoid basing major life choices on how similar things are to our own name. *T / F*

D READ FOR OUTCOMES Read the article again and take notes on ways to answer the questions.

1. What was the purpose of the experiment?
2. What were the main results?
3. What conclusions were drawn?
4. What do you think about the results of the experiment?

Glossary

neutral (adj) neither one thing nor its opposite
stage (v) make someone believe that something is real

E REFLECT Think about the answers to these questions.

1. Do you think that names could influence people to choose different careers? Why/Why not?
2. Can you think of any other ways that words can influence social behavior?

As expected, students who had been exposed to the 'rude' words interrupted the soonest, followed by the neutral group and, lastly, the students who had just processed 'polite' words.

John Bargh, who devised the experiment, admitted that we should not rush to the conclusion that exposure to rude or polite words makes us behave in that way. In fact, one of the problems with such a conclusion is that, in the experiment described above, 21 of the 34 participants did not interrupt at all in the 10 minutes that they were kept waiting. However, Bargh re-analyzed the results and looked only at those who had interrupted. Of these, over 60 percent had just processed the 'rude' words.

Is there more evidence to suggest that words play a more important role than we once thought? Pelham, Mirdenberg and Jones (2012) have suggested that our name – as one of the words that we learn first and hold dear – influences whether we like other people and things with similar names. In the most surprising results, it was shown that more people named Dennis had chosen dentistry as a profession. Similarly, more women named Laura, and more men named Lawrence, became lawyers. Similar links have been shown between a person's name and the place they choose to live, as well as their choice of a husband or wife.

LISTENING

A PREDICT Check (✓) the skills you think are important at school.

- passing exams ☐
- practical skills ☐
- developing your imagination ☐
- thinking independently ☐
- developing personal interests ☐
- artistic skills ☐
- physical exercise ☐

9.3 **B LISTEN FOR GIST** Listen to a conversation about education. Were any of your skills in Exercise A mentioned?

9.3 **C LISTEN FOR DETAIL** Listen again. Are these sentences true (T) or false (F)?

1 Cassie is new to the area. *T / F*

2 The Steiner education method places great emphasis on creativity. *T / F*

3 Rob and Cassie agree that passing exams is not a legitimate educational goal. *T / F*

4 Inspections at Rob and Sandy's school create tension. *T / F*

5 Steiner school courses are designed to meet the needs of individual students. *T / F*

6 The curriculum at the Steiner school is broadly similar to a mainstream school. *T / F*

9.4 **D LISTEN TO RAPID SPEECH** Listen to some extracts from the discussion. Cross out words and sounds that the speakers leave out. Put brackets [ ] around the phrases they link together. The first two have been done for you.

1 [Nice ~~to~~ meet ~~you~~.] How ~~are~~ ~~you~~ doing?

2 So … ~~have~~ you just moved here, Cassie?

3 I've lived here for … let me see … for four years.

4 Because it's you know … it's really *unique* and stuff.

5 Is it one of those places where you can, you know, do anything you want?

E REFLECT Think about the answers to these questions.

1 Which is the most important skill developed at school? Why?

2 How could secondary schools in your country be improved? Think of examples.

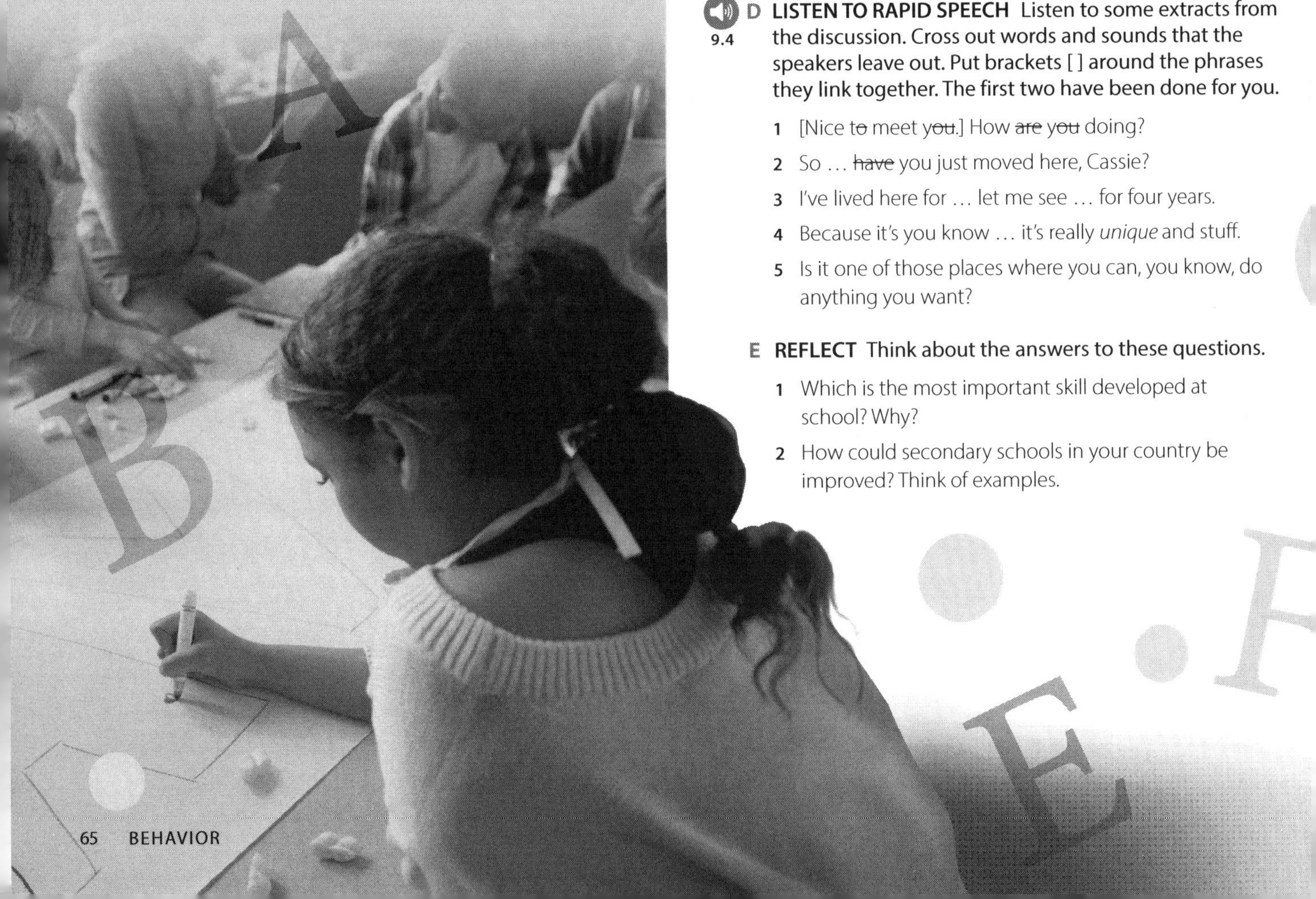

9.5 Behavior

Write a conclusion to an academic report

WRITING

A PREDICT Look at the pictures. What do you think it feels like to be in one of these crowds? Do people behave differently when they are in a crowd? Why?

B Read the conclusion to an academic report and match the topics (a–d) to the paragraphs (1–4).

- **a** Areas that still need investigation ___
- **b** Summary of theories researched ___
- **c** Aims of research ___
- **d** What was learned ___

C LINKING IN ACADEMIC WRITING Read the conclusion again and complete it with the linking words and phrases (a–e). Sometimes more than one option is possible.

- **a** However
- **b** On the other hand
- **c** Additionally
- **d** Nonetheless
- **e** Admittedly

D Underline two sentences where a colon is used to show that one idea explains another. Underline two sentences where a semi-colon is used to show that two related ideas are of equal importance.

WRITING PRACTICE

A PREPARE Choose a piece of academic research or use your imagination and take notes on the points you will make in your conclusion.

B PLAN You are going to write a conclusion to an academic report.

- Organize your notes from Exercise A into an appropriate structure for the conclusion to an academic report.
- Use linking words, colons and semi-colons to show the relationship between ideas.

C WRITE Write your conclusion in 200–300 words.

Conclusion

1 Our research set out to examine theories of crowd behavior, beginning with classic contagion and convergence theories, which have been the basis of all subsequent theories. It became clear that most of the research so far stems from disciplines such as psychology and sociology; there has been little recent research into crowd behavior at large outdoor events.

2 Contagion theory states that individuals are protected by their membership of the crowd and that individual responsibility is ignored: normal values and the ability to reason are abandoned. [1] ___, ideas and emotions within the crowd become contagious and spread rapidly. [2] ___, convergence theorists argue that individuals in a crowd do not lose personal identity: personal beliefs and values are communicated and crowd behavior depends on shared feelings and beliefs. [3] ___, some individuals may well exploit the anonymity of being in a crowd to take part in antisocial behaviors they normally would not.

3 It seems clear, then, that once individuals join a group they become part of a group personality. [4] ___, our research revealed that there are many factors that can influence the behavior of individuals in a crowd: crowd catalysts such as police presence, the space available, type of event and so on. We will be conducting further research in this area.

4 While both theories form the basis of most research into crowd behavior, they assume some kind of antisocial behavior is the outcome. They fail to demonstrate why some crowds remain passive and why individuals in a crowd who hold similar beliefs behave differently; nor do they examine the difference between organized and spontaneous crowds. [5] ___, we believe that these theories are still useful in understanding mass behavior in general.

VOCABULARY

Culture and heritage; Nouns with *to*

A Complete the sentences with the words in the box.

architectural designated endangered funds habitats heritage preserve refurbish ruins settlement

1 Some areas near the city have been ________ national parks so they can't be built on.

2 Because their ________ are threatened, many species are ________.

3 The unique ________ qualities of these buildings make them an important part of our country's ________.

4 The ________ found by archaeologists are said to be part of a ________ going back thousands of years.

5 We would like to at least ________ these houses to stop the damage getting worse until there are enough ________ available to ________ them.

B Complete the article with one word in each blank. The first and last letters and the number of letters needed are given to help you.

Building a future

For anyone who has the [1]**u**________**e** (*4*) to go into city planning, we need you – but don't expect an easy ride. What you need more than anything is the [2]**d**________**e** (*6*) to create better living conditions for city dwellers. It will be your [3]**r**________**y** (*14*) to make sure that the future does not become a nightmare scenario. You will have an [4]**o**________**n** (*10*) to future generations and you should be ready to improve things.

Why is it so hard? Well, historically, we have seen a [5]**f**________**e** (*7*) to learn from the mistakes of the past. We have also seen a flat [6]**r**________**l** (*7*) to adopt green measures and sometimes a general reluctance to think more than a few years into the future. There is a problem in that people often have a [7]**t**________**y** (*8*) to only do things that will benefit them in the short term. Sometimes, these people need a [8]**r**________**r** (*8*) to focus on long-term solutions as well.

PRONUNCIATION
Introducing new information

A Read the sentences aloud. Does the pitch go up or down on the underlined words?

1 I enjoyed getting to see some of the sights. And I made some great friends on my travels.
2 There's no doubt that travel broadens the mind. On the other hand, you won't learn much about a culture if you stay in a resort and never go exploring.
3 Some older vacationers tend to be happy with relaxed beach vacations and a bit of light sightseeing, whereas younger tourists usually want a little bit more action.
4 You're going to Cyprus? I love Cyprus. As a matter of fact, I was born there!
5 I know a lot of people find traveling exciting, but for me it's always really stressful.
6 I know tourism brings money to companies, but at the same time, I wonder how much ordinary people benefit from it.
7 I love traveling overseas. And it's good for the economy of the countries you visit.
8 Tourism isn't always beneficial to countries in many ways. And in fact, some resorts are now looking for ways to discourage big numbers of people.

10.1 **B** Listen to the sentences to check your answers to Exercise A.

GRAMMAR
Discourse markers

A Match numbers (1–10) to letters (a–j) to form full sentences.

1 There are so many European countries, for instance, ____
2 I don't like traveling very much. As a matter of fact, ____
3 We spent most of our trip in Bolivia. Conversely, ____
4 They cut their vacation short owing to the fact ____
5 I'm happy to fly everywhere, whereas ____
6 He claims he doesn't travel, yet ____
7 Some cities suffer from a big problem, namely, ____
8 I think it's the best museum in the world, ____
9 We enjoyed the sights despite ____
10 My summer in Spain was very relaxing. Moreover, ____

a he went on three vacations last year!
b that they were running out of money.
c I hate it!
d it really helped me get to grips with the language.
e the fact that there were huge crowds.
f the best I've been to in any case.
g that there are too many tourists.
h Belgium, that I still haven't visited.
i we only had two days in Venezuela.
j my husband says it's better to travel slowly by boat or train.

B Complete the second sentence so that it has a similar meaning to the first sentence. Write between two and five words, including the word given.

1 Although it was a long journey there, we enjoyed the view of the mountain immensely.
DESPITE
We enjoyed ourselves immensely ______________________
____
a long journey.

2 We didn't go to Warsaw, but it didn't matter because I've been there before.
CASE
We didn't go to Warsaw, but in ______________________
____
been there before.

3 There are two countries I really want to visit, and they are Australia and China.
NAMELY
There are two countries I really want to visit, ____________
______________________.

4 The bad weather prevented us from going to the national park.
OWING
We didn't go to the national park ______________________
______________________.

5 The return journey seemed very quick compared to the outward journey.
WHEREAS
The outward journey seemed to take a long time,
____
very quick.

6 To tell you the truth, I wouldn't mind if I never got on another plane in my life.
MATTER
______________________,
I wouldn't mind if I never got on another plane in my life.

VOCABULARY
Word building

A Choose the correct options (a, b or c) to complete the sentences.

1 She loves her job – she's very ___ about it.
- a passion
- b passionate
- c passionhood

2 Nobody knew the ___ of the mystery donor.
- a identity
- b identify
- c identification

3 I grew up in a really run-down ___.
- a neighborly
- b neighbor
- c neighborhood

4 Clark wanted to enter ___ life as soon as possible after graduating.
- a politics
- b politician
- c political

5 Some countries make you take a ___ test in order to adopt their nationality.
- a citizenship
- b citizen
- c citizenry

6 It was totally ___ of you to mention her brother – you know they don't speak to each other.
- a insensible
- b senseless
- c insensitive

7 Depositing huge sums of money in offshore accounts may be legal, but is it ___?
- a ethics
- b ethical
- c ethic

8 Charles is responsible for internet ___ at his company.
- a secure
- b securely
- c security

B Complete the text with words from the box with a correct suffix. Make any other necessary spelling changes.

apathy commune effect passion person persuade

To change the world quickly, you have to be 1 ________ about your beliefs, you need to have a(n) 2 ________ strategy and you need good 3 ________ skills – such as being extremely friendly, polite and, of course, 4 ________ – so that people will listen to you.

Sometimes, however, the best changes are the ones that take place little by little. If you can find a way to stop people from being 5 ________ and to make them care about their 6 ________, the results will slowly but surely become global.

GRAMMAR
Ellipsis and substitution

A Cross out any words that can be omitted.

1 Some people think we can change the world but I don't think we can change the world.
2 If you get the opportunity to go, you should take the opportunity to go.
3 A lot of people struggle with course fees and I wish they didn't struggle with course fees.
4 They should target governments and they should target large companies.
5 We're going to have food and we're going to have music.
6 You asked me if I thought we could make a difference and the answer is yes I do think we can make a difference.
7 I know a lot of people who are pessimistic about the future, but I'm not pessimistic about the future.
8 Are you joining us for pizza? Do you have any preference as to what we order?

B Complete the sentences with a phrase including *do*, *does*, *so* or *not*. Write one or two words in each blank.

1 I take a short vacation away from everything. I ________ to clear my head when I'm stressed at work.
2 He said he can't come, but I'm hoping he'll change his mind. Let me know if ________.
3 I might go to the stores later, so I'll let you know if ________.
4 Johnny went white-water rafting. I could never ________.
5 'Will you be finished before four?' I expect ________.'
6 You might need to access the archives. In order to ________, ask one of the technical support team.
7 'We might have to do this again.' 'I ________ – it took us days.'
8 'I'm planning to spend all my money on a sports car!' 'Why on Earth would you ________?'

PRONUNCIATION
Managing conversations

A Read the sentences aloud. Try to say the underlined words according to the instructions in parentheses. Pay attention to whether your intonation rises or falls.

1

A: So, then I plan to travel to Cambodia.

B: Right. (because you think the speaker has finished/you want to say something yourself)

2

A: The chairperson said there might be an opening for me.

B: OK. (showing excitement/enthusiasm)

3

A: There'd be a team of four initially, then six, then eight or more.

B: OK. (hesitant, needing clarification)

4

A: I think it's a great opportunity.

B: Right. (sarcastic, unenthusiastic)

5

A: I'm planning to apply for a job there.

B: I see! (genuinely interested)

10.2 **B Listen to the conversations from Exercise A. Do the speakers say the underlined words in the same way as you did?**

READING

A READ FOR GIST Read three short newspaper articles. Which urban problem(s) do they discuss?

B SYNTHESIZE INFORMATION Read the articles again. Complete the table using information from all three articles.

	Problems	Solutions	Criticism of solutions
UK			
Paris			
Freiburg			

Parking just got PRICIER

In another move to fight congestion and pollution in the UK's most gridlocked cities, councils may impose a workplace parking fee of up to $1000, to be paid for by employers rather than employees. Growing concerns about the effects of congestion and air pollution on residents' health, including asthma and bronchitis, have led to the move.

Some opponents of the plan say they have seen no evidence that fewer people were driving to work and that it could lead to job losses. Also it would force more people into using an already overcrowded public transportation system.

A spokesman for the Automobile Association (AA) said that instead of taxing businesses, who may be forced to leave the area or stop trading, we should be concentrating on getting people to switch to electric vehicles.

By law, all funds gained from such charges are to be invested in improving public transportation and infrastructure.

Paris' TRAFFIC PROBLEMS

The authorities in Paris have tried almost everything to reduc congestion and the mayor wants to reduce the number of ca entering the city by making life difficult for drivers.

With concerns raised about premature death due to a pollution, Paris has now made permanent a sticker syster All vehicles in Paris must display an anti-pollution sticker c face a fine of $68 for cars and $138 for trucks. The stickers co $4.18. Yet a recent police check found that only 1 in 50 vehicle stopped had the sticker.

About 600,000 vehicles drive around the city each day an most come in from the suburbs. Concerns have been raised b those traveling from the suburbs who are not as well connecte by the public transportation system. One driver complaine 'We're being taxed off the roads. It's not our fault. They shou get the car manufacturers to make cars that don't pollute.'

As green as it gets?

It is obviously easier to deal with urban problems in a small city with a population of fewer than half a million people, but maybe larger cities with traffic problems could take a page or two from Freiburg's book. For a start, the entire city center was pedestrianized back in 1973, and city authorities have developed an integrated system of 500 kilometers of bike routes, cable cars and a public transportation system that is efficient, comfortable and above all cheap. In fact, those who choose to live without a car at all are offered cheap housing and fre public transportation.

Preference is given to environmentally friendly mod of transportation such as wall biking and public transportati and smart urban planning ha made it a city of short distanc where people's needs can be within walking distance. All tl has made Freiburg one of the greenest and most pollution- cities in Europe.

Glossary

disincentive (n) a plan/action that makes you not want to do something
gridlocked (adj) with so much traffic congestion that vehicles cannot move at all
take a page out of/from somebody's book (idiom) to copy somebody else's actions because they are successful

C REFLECT Is it worth owning a car in a big city?

LISTENING

A PREDICT Read the ad. Would you be interested in applying for this job? What skills would you need? What might be the challenges of this kind of work?

Research Assistant – Galapagos National Park, Ecuador

We are looking for a research assistant with a background in science. You must be physically fit, capable of working outside in extreme weather and available to work flexible hours. Salary depending on experience. Accommodations provided.

10.3 **B LISTEN FOR MAIN IDEA** Listen to the conversation and answer the questions.

1 What are the woman and man waiting for?

____

2 What are they both a little worried about?

____

3 What are they both positive about?

____

10.4 **C LISTEN FOR SPECIFIC INFORMATION** Listen to Jonathan's interview and complete the application form with one or two words in each blank.

10.5 **D LISTEN TO REGISTER** Jonathan used different registers to speak to Antonia and, later, to Dr. Ramsey. Listen to some extracts. In each case, decide how Jonathan could say the same thing in a different register.

1 ______________________

2 ______________________

3 ______________________

4 ______________________

10.6 **E** Now listen to how Jonathan says similar things in a different register and check your answers to Exercise D.

F REFLECT Think about the answers to these questions.

1 What are the most difficult things about living in an isolated place?

2 Do you frequently change register in your own language? Why?

Research Assistant – Galapagos National Park

Name : Jonathan Wheeler

Qualification(s) : Degree in [1] ______________

Studied at : University of [2] ______________ Anglia

Relevant experience :

- [3] ______________ months working for Nature Trust on the Isle of Skye
- Field trip: Northumberland, studying [4] ______________ of various species of birds
- Field trip: Forest of Dean, studying breeding habits of native [5] ______________
- Practical skills: maintenance work – fixing fences and maintenance of [6] ______________

In the space provided, please state what appeals to you about the Galapagos National Park:

I think it's essential that we [7] ______________ nature as much as we can and, for me, this is a great opportunity to study a relatively unspoiled area. I think that tourism and industry are [8] ______________ so much of nature. It's vital that we conduct [9] ______________ while we still can, in the hope that we can protect wildlife.

WRITING

A Read the title of the essay. What are some of the pros and cons of tourism?

B Read the whole essay and answer the questions.

1 What is the writer's opinion of tourism?

2 What arguments does the writer use to support their opinions?

3 Does the writer mention any positive aspects of mass tourism?

C **USING COUNTER-ARGUMENTS AND REBUTTALS** Read the essay again and answer the questions.

1 Which paragraph includes examples of counter-arguments (i.e. stating an opposing position) and rebuttals (i.e. stating why you believe an argument is incorrect)?

2 What is the counter-argument and what is the rebuttal? Does the rebuttal directly answer the counter-argument?

3 What phrases are used to introduce the counter-argument and rebuttal?

WRITING PRACTICE

A **PREPARE** Read this essay title and write some notes on each of the points.

Do shopping malls have a positive or negative impact on local communities?

- job opportunities
- prices
- convenience
- local businesses
- environmental impact

B **PLAN** You are going to write a persuasive essay in answer to the task above.

- Organize your notes from Exercise A into an appropriate structure for a persuasive essay.
- Use a counter-argument and rebuttal in the third or fourth paragraph.

C **WRITE** Write your essay in 220–260 words.

Does tourism have a POSITIVE OR NEGATIVE IMPACT?

1 Cheap air travel has opened up the world to more and more people and few countries are unaffected by mass tourism. Many argue that this is a good thing – that it promotes understanding of different cultures and makes international connections. However, I believe that in the long term, tourism has a negative impact, spoiling the very places it promotes.

2 First, there is the environmental damage mass tourism brings with it. Ugly hotels built near traditional architecture, increased traffic congestion bringing pollution, more litter and waste to dispose of; the list goes on. Even if tourists do behave responsibly, sheer numbers can cause problems, such as damage to ancient buildings and monuments.

3 Mass tourism can also damage the heart and soul of a tourist destination by making it just like any other vacation resort. Cultural history and heritage are reduced to a spectacle for visitors, and tourists often lack respect for local traditions and culture, ignoring local codes of behavior and upsetting the local community. It leads, therefore, to the opposite of promoting understanding between cultures.

4 There is an argument that mass tourism has a beneficial impact because it brings in money and creates new jobs. Hotels, stores and restaurants all need staffing. While this is true up to a point, it should be remembered that many of these jobs are low-skilled and are often seasonal and insecure with no benefits such as pensions, sick pay or healthcare. Also, most of the tourism industry is owned by big foreign companies: they get the profits, while local businesses receive little benefit.

5 In conclusion, the long-term effects of mass tourism are largely negative. It can impact negatively on the environment, damage or destroy local cultures and traditions, the jobs it provides are insecure and short-lived, and local businesses suffer while the profits go to foreign corporations.

Irregular Verbs

Base form	Simple past	Past participle
be	was/were	been
become	became	become
begin	began	begun
break	broke	broken
bring	brought	brought
build	built	built
buy	bought	bought
can	could	been able to
catch	caught	caught
choose	chose	chosen
come	came	come
cost	cost	cost
cut	cut	cut
drink	drank	drunk
eat	ate	eaten
fall	fell	fallen
feel	felt	felt
find	found	found
forget	forgot	forgotten
get	got	got
give	gave	given
go	went	gone/been
grow	grew	grown
have	had	had
hear	heard	heard
hit	hit	hit
hold	held	held
hurt	hurt	hurt
keep	kept	kept
know	knew	known
leave	left	left
lend	lent	lent
let	let	let

Base form	Simple past	Past participle
lose	lost	lost
make	made	made
mean	meant	meant
meet	met	met
must	had to	had to
pay	paid	paid
put	put	put
read	read	read
ride	rode	ridden
run	ran	run
say	said	said
see	saw	seen
sell	sold	sold
send	sent	sent
set	set	set
shut	shut	shut
sing	sang	sung
sit	sat	sat
sleep	slept	slept
speak	spoke	spoken
spell	spelled	spelled
spend	spent	spent
stand	stood	stood
steal	stole	stolen
take	took	taken
teach	taught	taught
tell	told	told
think	thought	thought
throw	threw	thrown
understand	understood	understood
wear	wore	worn
win	won	won
write	wrote	written

PHONETIC SYMBOLS											
Single vowels			Diphthongs			Consonants					
/ɪ/	fish	/fɪʃ/	/uw/	news	/nuw/	/p/	pen	/pen/	/s/	snake	/sneɪk/
/iː/	bean	/biːn/	/eɪ/	face	/feɪs/	/b/	bag	/bæg/	/z/	zoo	/zuː/
/ʊ/	foot	/fʊt/	/ɔɪ/	boy	/bɔɪ/	/t/	tea	/tiː/	/ʃ/	shop	/ʃɒp/
/uː/	shoe	/ʃuː/	/oʊ/	nose	/noʊz/	/d/	dog	/dɒg/	/ʒ/	television	/'telɪvɪʒən/
/e/	egg	/eg/	/ju/	use	/juz/	/ʧ/	chip	/ʧɪp/	/m/	map	/mæp/
/ə/	mother	/'mʌðər/	/aɪ/	eye	/aɪ/	/ʤ/	jazz	/ʤæz/	/n/	name	/neɪm/
/ɜː/	word	/wɜːrd/	/aʊ/	mouth	/maʊθ/	/k/	cake	/keɪk/	/ŋ/	ring	/rɪŋ/
/ɔː/	talk	/tɔːk/				/g/	girl	/gɜːrl/	/h/	house	/haʊs/
/æ/	back	/bæk/				/f/	film	/fɪlm/	/l/	leg	/leg/
/ʌ/	bus	/bʌs/				/v/	verb	/vɜːrb/	/r/	road	/roʊd/
/ɑː/	arm	/ɑːrm/				/θ/	thing	/θɪŋ/	/w/	want	/wɒnt/
/ɒ/	top	/tɒp/				/ð/	these	/ðiːz/	/j/	yes	/jes/

UNIT 6

Lesson 6.4, Listening, Exercise B

6.3 Perhaps one of the most well-known figures in modern British history is the explorer, Robert Falcon Scott. Tragically, he is not famous for his achievement, but for his failure. Scott headed an expedition whose goal was to reach the South Pole before anyone else. On January 17, 1912, Scott, with four companions, finally reached the South Pole, only to discover that a Norwegian party, led by Roald Amundsen, had beaten them to it – by just 34 days. Scott and his men died on their journey home.

Lesson 6.4, Listening, Exercise C

6.4 From *the* mid-19th century, a number of expeditions had traveled to Antarctica to try and map its extent and find out more about the wildlife and plantlife of this unknown territory. The men who undertook these journeys suffered terrible hardship; sickness, injury, hunger *and* cold were part of their everyday experience. Every single item which the explorers needed *had* to be transported by ship. Then the provisions had to be carried across *the* ice. These included tents, sleeping bags, building materials, food for men and animals, heating oil, bedding, clothing *and* scientific equipment.

Both Scott and Amundsen set out for *their* final trek to the South Pole within a few weeks of each other. Amundsen's journey *went* smoothly, and his entire team returned safe and sound a month later. In contrast, as *we* have already learned, Scott and his companions were beaten to their goal and ultimately lost their lives. *What* factors led to these *two* totally different results?

Amundsen's only goal was to reach the South Pole before anyone else. In contrast, Scott's expedition *was* meant to be a voyage of scientific discovery and he put together a large scientific team including a zoologist, meteorologist, geologists and biologists. Some experts believe *that* Amundsen's clear focus on a single goal was key to his success.

Scott planned to use a mixture of transportation – motor sleds, pony and *dog* sleds and 'man-hauling', in other words, the men themselves pulling sleds. *The* first motor sled broke down before they even set out, the second fell through the ice, and the third broke down shortly afterwards. The ponies were totally unsuited *to* the climate and the heavy work and they all died of cold and hunger. The dogs *were* better-suited to the conditions, but they were worked so hard, and fed so little, that they too died eventually. By contrast, Amundsen's expedition relied entirely *on the best Antarctic transportation at the time*: dog sleds. *He* hired experienced dog drivers and made sure his dogs were fed properly and only traveled for short distances every day.

Amundsen embarked *on* his final trek to the Pole from a point much closer than Scott. Advance parties *marked* almost the entire length of the route with flags and frequent food depots which were clearly marked so that they could not be missed by the men in the mist and snow. Scott's *food* depots were located far less frequently. Scott's team frequently lost *their* way and often had difficulty locating these. *The* food which Scott provided was not adequate for his team's needs. Some of the group were *suffering* from 'scurvy', a condition caused by lack of vitamins which slowly but surely weakens physical strength. Amundsen had taken care of providing enough food, including *a* specially designed mixture which contained vitamins. He supplemented this diet with *fresh seal meat*.

While Scott's story has become a legend of British history, Amundsen's *clear* thinking, expert planning, training and experience meant that he succeeded in his expedition.

UNIT 7

Lesson 7.4, Listening, Exercise B

7.3 **C = Caroline T = Thomas**

C: Welcome to *Beyond Brave* with me Caroline Spencer. Today, Thomas Bennett is here to talk to us about tightrope walking. Why has it become such a popular topic recently?

T: Well, what has brought it to public attention is the exploits of contemporary performers such as Nik Wallenda and Philippe Petit.

C: Tell us something about these two extraordinary people.

T: You might say that Nik Wallenda has tightrope walking in his blood. He represents the latest generation of a family who have been circus performers since the 1700s. It was his great-grandfather, Karl Wallenda, who perfected circus acts including the human pyramid, as well as high-wire walking and cycling. He was killed attempting to walk between two skyscrapers in 1978. That's probably why Nik has devoted his life to tightrope walking. In 2011, he successfully completed the same walk in honor of his great-grandfather.

C: Incredible! I find him a very charismatic figure. But he also uses the power of the media to his advantage, doesn't he?

T: Oh yes. I think it's partly as a result of his relationship with TV networks that his exploits have reached such a wide audience. It's been estimated that 16 million people watched his walk across Niagara Falls on live television.

C: You mentioned another great tightrope artist, Philippe Petit, earlier? His accomplishments were made into a film, weren't they?

T: That's right. *Man on Wire* won the Oscar for best documentary in 2008.

C: It's a somewhat obscure thing to make a documentary about, isn't it?

T: Well, yes it is. And to be honest, if the film hadn't been made, I don't think there would have been so much interest in the whole idea of tightrope walking. The film tells the story of Petit's 1974 high-wire walk between the Twin Towers of New York's World Trade Center. His incredibly daring – and I might add illegal – achievement was the focus of the film.

C: What do you mean 'illegal'?

T: Well, because the stunt was so incredibly dangerous. I mean … the guy was going to walk across a wire just two and a half centimeters wide, across a distance of nearly 40 meters which was … wait for it … more than 400 meters above the ground. If anything had gone wrong, well – the consequences would have been utterly dreadful.

And New York City didn't want to be associated with the possibly tragic result of such an event, so obviously they never gave Petit permission to carry out the stunt. So, the preparations had to be done in secret – examining the site, installing the equipment, the timings, everything. It was a bit like one of those classic bank heists you see in the movies! He and his team had to get up the two towers in secret, fire a guiding rope from one tower to the other with a bow and arrow …

C: A bow and arrow?!

T: That's right! And then Petit crossed – not just once, but four times – backwards and forwards across the wire while a crowd of thousands gathered below and watched in terrified astonishment. After he'd completed the feat, he was arrested by waiting police officers. The police released him pretty soon afterwards though.

C: And there's been a more recent movie, hasn't there?

T: The 2015 movie *The Wire* is a biographical drama of the same story. It's thanks to this that younger people are taking a renewed interest.

UNIT 8

Lesson 8.4, Listening, Exercise B
.3 **S = Scott A = Angela**

S: Today, we're going to be broadcasting live from a space training facility in Germany. With me is scientist and researcher, Angela Schneider.

A: Good morning, Scott. It's a pleasure to be able to talk to you and your listeners.

S: So, what do you do exactly, Angela?

A: I'm a nutritionist by training and over the last few years, I've specialized in research into the effects of a zero-gravity environment on the human body. Good nutrition is critical for human health and of course this is true for those traveling in space, too. It's important that astronauts have a specially designed diet which gives them exactly the right number of calories which they need to do their work and the correct balance of vitamins and nutrients for optimum performance and well-being.

S: What problems do astronauts face in terms of their physical health?

A: Astronauts are known to lose bone density during any extended stay in space, and this means they are at an increased risk of bone fractures once they return to Earth, so we've been looking at ways of dealing with that problem. New diet programs include vitamin D and calcium supplements. In addition, astronauts follow a program of resistance training, which has been proved to be very effective in preventing bone density loss.

S: What other nutrients are important?

A: That's an interesting question, Scott. Another essential nutrient that we've been studying is iron. As I'm sure you and your listeners know, iron deficiency in the blood can lead to anemia – where you don't have enough red blood cells. Some of the symptoms of anemia are fatigue, dizziness and headaches. So, we were focusing on making sure that our astronauts had enough iron in their diet, but we've come to the surprising conclusion that actually, they end up with an *excessive* amount of iron in their blood as a result of living in space for long periods of time. So, we're looking to actually reduce the iron content in the foods which we provide for our crews.

S: So … less of the spinach eh?

A: That's right! And as well as these vital scientific aspects, we have to make the food palatable for the men and women who are working in space. In the past, some astronauts have complained that the food – in the shape of bite-sized cubes, powders and freeze-dried foodstuffs – was unappetizing and bland. Today, we offer foods which are cutting-edge in terms of the latest scientific research, but which are also … well, really tasty actually.

S: Can you give us some examples of what an astronaut might expect to find on the menu here?

A: Um … let me see. Duck breast with capers, lobster, chocolate cake …

S: No! Really?

A: Yes, really. We've teamed up with chefs to come up with really delicious dishes. We even have a 'special occasion' menu for birthdays or when there's a change of crew.

S: That's amazing! Well, Angela. It's been absolutely fascinating to talk to you. Thanks so much.

A: Thank *you*!

UNIT 9

Lesson 9.4, Listening, Exercise B
9.3 **R = Rob S = Sandy C = Cassie**

R: All right, Sandy? What's up?

S: Hi Rob. This is my friend Cassie.

R: Hi, Cassie. Nice to meet you. How are you doing?

C: Good, thanks.

R: So … you just moved here, Cassie?

C: No, actually. I've lived here for … let me see … for four years.

R: So how come you don't go to our school?

C: I go to a Steiner school.

S: How cool is that? Like – *so* awesome!

R: Um … well, I don't mean to be rude or anything, but … why's that 'awesome' exactly?

S: Cos it's you know … it's really *unique* and stuff. Go on Cassie. Tell Rob all about your school.

C: No, it's OK. You probably don't want to hear about it anyway.

R: Yes … no … I mean, course I want to hear about it.

C: Well, the … you know … philosophy behind the school is that education is about more than just passing exams and learning a ton of stuff.

S: That's *so* true!

C: So, the idea is that you develop as a, well, a whole person. The school is supposed to develop your artistic and practical skills as well as your intellectual ones. Probably *the* most important thing is imagination. You learn to be a responsible … human being.

R: Yeah, right!

S: Be quiet, Rob!

C: Yeah, sounds silly I know …

S: No, no. Not at all. Don't take any notice of Rob. *I* think it sounds fantastic. I mean … at our school there's a huge amount of pressure on us to study and pass exams.

R: Hang on. You're right – there *is* a lot of pressure, but I mean – like – I'd be bummed if I didn't get the grades I want to go to college. So, there *is* a reason behind the pressure.

S: Yeah, but it's too much. Even the teachers are under pressure. If we don't get good exam grades, then they get into a lot of trouble. These inspectors come around every semester and check *everything*.

R: Anyway, tell us some more about *your* school. Is it one of those places where you can, you know, do anything you want? Mess around all day? Not go to lessons.

C: No, it's not like that at all. Maybe I'm not explaining it well. It's more to do with *who you are*. For instance, we're not in classes according to our age – everybody lumped in together just because their birthdays happen to be in the same year. We're grouped according to our interests and stage of development. Each person is treated differently, and you can learn at your own pace and in a way that suits you.

S: Do you have assembly in the morning, like we do?

C: No, we start the day with group exercises, recitals and songs. It's supposed to put you in the mood to learn – forget any negative thoughts, get in the right space to really focus. Then we have a two-hour lesson which is always based on one topic. It's not like – first, math, then geography, then English–like most other schools.

R: So, why's it called 'Steiner' anyway?

C: Rudolf Steiner was the founder of the whole … philosophy … the system. He was this Austrian guy who lived in … I'm not sure … at the beginning of the 20th century anyway. Today, there are hundreds of Steiner schools all over the world.

S: I think you're so lucky, Cassie. I wish I could go to your school.

UNIT 10

Lesson 10.4, Listening, Exercise B
10.3 **J = Jonathan A = Antonia**

J: Hiya. Jonathan. How you doing?

A: All right? I'm Antonia. You here for the interview?

J: Yep. Been waiting long?

A: Nah – 'bout five minutes. There's tea and coffee here. D'you want something?

J: Yeah, I wouldn't mind a cup.

A: Got it.

J: Great.

A: So … we're both up for the same job?

J: Yeah. You done anything like this before?

A: No. You?

J: Well, I've studied – conservation I mean, so I've done a lot of field trips and stuff. I spent last summer working on the Isle of Skye in Scotland. But the Galapagos …

A: What? I've never been to either. I guess you have a better idea of what the job will involve – if you lived in Skye?

J: Well, it's a commitment. It's somewhat cut off. I know you can fly into Puerto Ayora and then take a boat, but it's expensive and sometimes, the water taxis don't run. That's my only hesitation … It's a bit of an isolated place to live all year round.

A: You can say that again. It bothers me a little bit, too, if I'm honest. I heard they have a tendency to cancel flights and boats because of bad weather. You know I, um, I'm not sure how I feel about that.

J: Yeah. You're right. The job looks great though. Everything I love doing. But I have no desire to be stuck there!

A: Yes, what a great thing to spend your time doing. You know … looking on the bright side.

Lesson 10.4, Listening, Exercise C
10.4 **D = Dr. Ramsey J = Jonathan**

D: Jonathan Wheeler?

J: Hello Dr. Ramsey. How do you do?

D: Good morning, Jonathan. Would you like to come on through? Can I get you anything? Tea? Coffee?

J: A glass of water would be great, thank you.

D: Please have a seat. So … you've just graduated. Tell me more!

J: Yes, that's right. I have a degree in environmental science from the University of East Anglia and actually have practical experience from several field trips.

D: And I see that you worked with the Nature Trust on the Isle of Skye last year. So, you've worked in a remote area before?

J: Yes, that's correct. I was there for two months. It was fascinating.

D: And your field trips … one was studying birds in Northumberland …

J: Yes, we studied their natural habitats.

D: And you also went to the Forest of Dean.

J: Yes … to study the breeding patterns of the deer that live there.

D: Well, that's all good experience. How did you find the physical side of things? The post requires you to be physically fit – out in all weather – that kind of thing.

J: Oh, I like hard work. I've done a lot of fencing, maintaining paths … that kind of thing.

D: OK. And I see here at the bottom of your form that you're very much committed to the environment and nature – you want to preserve it, you say here.

J: Yes, I think a lot of things are endangering so much of the environment – for instance, things like tourism and industry – and it's happening very quickly. So, while there is still time, I think we should carry out research and … hopefully … we will protect the wildlife we have – keep it for future generations.

D: One last question. What attracted you to this job in particular?

J: I really feel that the job is an ideal opportunity for me, and it involves everything that I enjoy doing.

6.1 Challenging journeys

VOCABULARY

A

1 uncharted
2 impenetrable
3 globetrotters
4 embarked
5 heart
6 provisions
7 long-haul
8 beaten

B

1 off
2 for
3 round
4 against
5 back
6 out
7 up
8 from

GRAMMAR

A

1 can't
2 might
3 likely
4 may have decided
5 have
6 possibility
7 must
8 may well

B

1 may well have
2 extremely probable/likely that
3 must have left
4 might have forgotten
5 a distinct possibility
6 can't have been

6.2 Inquisitive minds

GRAMMAR

A

1 reading
2 to spread
3 to maintain
4 to do
5 telling

B

1 c 2 d 3 e 4 a 5 b 6 f

C

1 b 2 a

VOCABULARY

A

1 quiet
2 By
3 take
4 greet
5 away
6 order
7 tidy
8 tear

B

1 and wide
2 to-riches
3 and soul
4 after time
5 to back
6 but surely
7 by side
8 or-/and-death

6.3 Reading

READING

C

1 Because of the success and recognition his trip to Sumatra had brought him
2 Being taken prisoner and lack of supplies (getting sick only happened after he had decided to turn back)
3 He was either very optimistic and determined or he wanted to hide his misfortunes.
4 They also disappeared.

6.4 Listening

LISTENING

B

Possible answers

1 (Robert Falcon) Scott and (Roald) Amundsen
2 to (be the first to) reach the South Pole
3 January 1912 and 1911: the speaker says that Amundsen reached the South Pole 34 days earlier
4 Amundsen reached the South Pole first; Scott and his men died on the return journey

C

Historical background
Goals
Route planning
Food and nutrition
Transportation

D

Possible answers

1 to map the area and study it
2 It was very hard – sickness, injury, hunger and cold.
3 tents, sleeping bags, building materials, food, fuel, bedding, clothing, scientific equipment
4 Scott – to study the area and to reach the South Pole; Amundsen – only to reach the South Pole
5 motor sleds, pony and dog sleds, man-hauling

6 the motor sleds didn't work, the ponies died, he didn't know how to handle the dogs
7 carefully, using flags and clearly marked food depots
8 he didn't allow enough calories per man; he didn't include any vitamins in the diet

6.5 Write an expository essay

WRITING

B
1 c 2 e 3 a 4 b 5 d

C
1 a 2 c 3 d 4 e 5 b

WRITING PRACTICE

C
Model answer
Travel broadens the mind, they say, and I believe this to be generally true. Some people are apprehensive about finding themselves in unfamiliar places, but life is supposed to be an adventure. Three of the many benefits of travel are learning about the world, reaching a better understanding of your own country and teaching you about yourself.

First, travel can teach you more about the world than any book, because you are experiencing the culture of another country first-hand. Engaging with the local people, you learn about their history and traditions, habits, food and even the way they think.

Second, it forces you to make comparisons – how your own culture differs from the one you are visiting. You will notice the cultural differences and see what makes your home country unique. In short, having traveled, you will see your own country with new eyes.

Finally, you can learn a lot about yourself by traveling. You will learn how you cope with unfamiliar situations, how you react to strange habits and customs. You will also learn about how much you are able to tolerate. Traveling will also test your language and social skills. You will return home a different person if you have fully immersed yourself in the experience of traveling.

In summary, traveling is a whole education in itself. The benefits gained from travel and experiencing other countries first-hand – greater knowledge of the world and how people do things differently (or the same), a new perspective on your own country and the self-knowledge gained – are immeasurable. In addition, you will have memories to treasure for a lifetime.

7.1 Beyond the limits

GRAMMAR

A
1 wasn't 2 that/which 3 it 4 it's 5 to 6 who/that
7 when 8 that/when

B
Possible answers
1 It was to raise money for charity that I applied to run the race.
2 It's the psychological not the physical challenge that's a problem for me!
3 It's only now that I've been running for five days that I've noticed the pain in my legs.
4 It was my sister who persuaded me to enter the race.
5 It wasn't a marathon that I ran – it was an ultramarathon!

C
Possible answers
1 It was the landscape paintings that they really wanted to see.
2 It was him who/that was to blame for breaking the window, not her.
3 It was the part at the end that Steven didn't understand.
4 It's you (that) I'm talking to!
5 It's the cost that bothers me.
6 It was because Eliza was scared that she said 'no'.
7 It's (only) when/after something's gone that you really appreciate it.
8 It was only when I got back that I realized how dangerous it was. / It wasn't until I got back that I realized how dangerous it was.

VOCABULARY

A
1 disgusted
2 resilient
3 superior
4 humble
5 devastated
6 courageous

B
1 courageous
2 humble
3 devastated
4 frustrated/grumpy
5 indifferent
6 superior
7 grumpy
8 hysterical

PRONUNCIATION

A
1 ↘ falling
2 ↗ rising
3 ↗ rising
4 ↘ falling
5 ↘ falling
6 ↗ rising

7.2 Extreme jobs

VOCABULARY

A
1 land 2 sick 3 competition 4 pressure 5 application
6 conditions

B
1 immensely
2 utterly
3 altogether

4 noticeably
5 relatively
6 remarkably
7 outright
8 radically
9 practically
10 somewhat

GRAMMAR

A

1 What ~~that~~ happened was I got confused.
2 Why ~~crashed~~ the computer **crashed** I have no idea!
3 Pets are easy – **all** they ~~all~~ need is food, water and some attention.
4 **What** ~~That~~ Lara likes about summer is being able to sleep on the balcony.
5 **All you** ~~You all~~ need is a snack and some good company.
6 **That's what** ~~What's that~~ Simon can't stand about this job – the silly rules!
7 **What** ~~That~~ we ended up doing was taking the train.
8 I didn't have my phone on me so what **I** did ~~I do~~ was ask a colleague to borrow hers.

B

1 What they did in the end was turn back.
2 All we need is a map.
3 What I can't stand is sleeping in a tent.
4 What Rex loves is playing with his ball in the yard.
5 All they needed was a drink of water.
6 What you need is a vacation.
7 What Tanya wanted more than anything was to be a ballerina.
8 All she's asking for is a short break.

C

1 What she loves most about
2 All (that) she wants is a
3 what he did was call
4 What I can't stand about/stand when
5 What I've realized is
6 All my sister remembers

PRONUNCIATION

A

1 The movie was <u>really</u> amazing, actually – we loved it!
2 I don't want <u>any</u> old doctor – I want the one I always see.
3 The questions they asked me were <u>really</u> ridiculous!
4 Any questions you have will be answered at the end, OK?
5 Well, you don't tell your password to just <u>any</u>body.
6 Let's go – <u>any</u>where's better than here!
7 The test was <u>really</u> hard but he thinks he passed.
8 'Which movie do you want to watch?''Oh, <u>any</u> one. You choose.'

7.3 Reading

READING

B

Possible answers

1 drowning
2 It is the greatest sensual experience.
3 that it is a life spent traveling and having fun in exotic places
4 only if you are in the top rank and have sponsorships and endorsements

C

1 It
2 you
3 such incidents
4 Which
5 one
6 Many
7 that
8 those who
9 it's
10 that

D

1 surfing; C
2 the reader/people in general; E
3 shark attacks; A
4 dangers/riptides; A
5 a wave; A
6 surfers; E
7 surfing big waves/catching a wave as tall as a tower; A
8 non-surfers/onlookers; E
9 the lifestyle; A
10 prize money; A

7.4 Listening

LISTENING

B

1 circus
2 1978
3 16 million
4 documentary
5 New York
6 40
7 in secret
8 bow and arrow

C

1 b
2 c
3 c
4 a

7.5 Write a cover letter

WRITING

B

2 climbing ability; skill in the use and maintenance of power tools; working at height; calmness in tense situations; ability to follow instructions and to work well with others

C

Possible answers

1 led/managed
2 tasked with collecting
3 managed
4 oversaw/coordinated/organized
5 I (also) developed

WRITING PRACTICE

C

Model answer

Dear Mr. Scholes,

I am writing to apply for the position of Lifeguard Team Leader at Ocean Resorts.

You will see from my résumé (attached) that I have four years' experience as a beach lifeguard in Australia, where I headed up a team of 20 lifeguards and coordinated sea and air rescue services when necessary. I have rescued swimmers from shark attacks on several occasions, so am able to work under pressure. During that time, I trained as a paramedic and have a good knowledge of first aid.

I have a lifesaving certification from Australia and since coming to this country have acquired an RLSS certification. In fact, I achieved the highest grade of my intake. I have worked poolside at a spa here for three years, and my duties included liaising with customer care and sometimes helping with front-of-house duties. Although I am no longer part of the Australian 4x4 medley relay team, I have kept up my training regimen and remain as strong a swimmer as ever.
I look forward to your response.

Best regards,
Bruce MacNamara

8.1 Health and wellness

VOCABULARY

A

1 sore
2 rash
3 rate
4 pressure
5 sprained
6 fractured
7 pulled
8 dislocate

B

1 fractured
2 pulled
3 inflamed
4 rate
5 sore
6 sprained
7 rash
8 blood

GRAMMAR

A

1 into
2 in
3 to
4 To/With
5 with/in
6 to
7 of/about
8 among/of

B

1 the person whose fitness business is now worth millions
2 the person (who) I trust more than anyone
3 whereby it is impossible for me to get a virus
4 a training injury from which you might never recover
5 people for whom exercise is not a priority
6 into whose pockets the profits all go, is very satisfied

8.2 Sports and wellness

VOCABULARY

A

1 gut feeling
2 gave him food for thought
3 got cold feet
4 give it his best shot
5 out of his depth
6 throwing in the towel

B

1 fizzy
2 Crunchy/Crisp
3 sour
4 mild
5 appetizing
6 creamy/cheesy
7 tangy; acidic
8 bland
9 soggy

PRONUNCIATION

A

1 isn't really my cup of tea
2 made a meal of it
3 keep an eye out
4 with a grain of salt
5 head and shoulders above
6 moving the goalposts

GRAMMAR

A

1 more
2 either
3 Most people
4 some
5 others
6 very few
7 of
8 little

B

1 When you're doing a serious hike, you can't drink too much ~~of~~ water – in fact, most people don't drink enough.
2 There were two vegan options, but I didn't want **either** ~~both~~ of them.
3 **Those** ~~They~~ who followed the diet reported an average loss of three kilos in the first week.
4 You have too much sugar and salt in your diet – it's best if you cut back on **both** ~~neither~~.
5 There are only **a** / ~~only~~ **very** few restaurants that serve good vegetarian food in this city.
6 You drink a lot of coffee, and I think you'd sleep better if you drank less ~~of~~.
7 These are your books – **mine** ~~my~~ are still over there where I left them.
8 Jamie only needs six hours of sleep a night, but I can never seem to get enough ~~of~~.

8.3 Reading

READING

A

Charcoal – c
Ketogenic – a
Cauliflower – d
Vegan – b

B

1 the keto diet
2 the vegan diet
3 the charcoal diet

C

Possible answers

1 Interestingly; Admittedly
2 supposedly; allegedly
3 positive attitude: There's no doubt
neutral attitude: It is also thought to
skeptical attitude: it seems
4 colloquial asides: I don't know about you
tag questions: Sounds rather scientific, doesn't it?
rhetorical questions: Black cheese … anyone?

8.4 Listening

LISTENING

C

1 b 2 a 3 a 4 a

D

1 right amount of calories; vitamins; nutrients; vitamin D; supplements
2 bone fractures
3 resistance training
4 excessive
5 duck breast; capers; lobster; chocolate cake

8.5 Write a summary

WRITING

B

Possible answers

1 'overtraining syndrome'; symptoms; physiological; psychological
2 Summary a misses the point and is irrelevant.
Summary b is the best because it includes the key points, phrased clearly in the writer's own words and without changing the original meaning.
Summary c repeats language from the text almost word for word.

C

Possible answers

1 increased heart rate; weight loss; excessive thirst
2 the negative physical effects of overtraining
3 The physical symptoms of overtraining to look out for are loss of both weight and muscle, inability to put on muscle and constant thirst. Further symptoms include an increase in heart rate, fluctuations in blood pressure, injury and susceptibility to infections.

WRITING PRACTICE

C

Model answer

Physical symptoms of overtraining syndrome include loss of both weight and muscle, inability to put on muscle and constant thirst. Psychological symptoms include a lack of readiness for training, sleeping problems and tiredness, changes in mood and a loss of confidence. Overtraining syndrome can be treated by identifying symptoms, seeking medical help and adopting a varied training regime with periods of rest.

9.1 Language and behavior

VOCABULARY

A

1 stoked
2 whining
3 bloke; dude
4 shady; stolen
5 TV; like; wheels

B

1 shambles 2 crashed 3 could do with 4 set her back
5 grand 6 bucks 7 broke 8 in good shape

PRONUNCIATION

A

1 I feel kind of strange – like I've been here before or something.
2 We have to give a talk, or a speech, or something like that.
3 I have to do some jobs – shopping, cleaning and so on.
4 You know, I think that, in some way or another, he must be involved.
5 So, in a sense, this is the easiest job in the world!
6 What do you take me for – some sort of fool?
7 Don't give me excuses like you overslept or whatever.
8 My course covers health and safety issues, stuff like that.

GRAMMAR

A

1 Those students who haven't completed the assignment should stay behind at the end of the lecture.
2 Both of the solutions he suggested sounded a little like a desperate attempt to please the boss.
3 He invested all the money he'd saved up into some crazy get-rich-quick scheme and lost everything.
4 The thing that annoys Pierre most is the way young people don't seem to care about language.
5 Three of the 20 people present were first-time attendees.
6 The idea that simply punishing children teaches them to behave has fallen out of favor with many modern educationalists.
7 Do you know a good place to eat that would suit a group of hungry teenagers?
8 Sometimes it seems to me that almost everyone I know is hooked on some computer game or other.

B

1 I spend **almost** all my free time ~~almost~~ doing sports.
2 The belief **that** ~~what~~ you can change things is all you need in order to make a difference.
3 The person (**who/that**) ~~where~~ I spoke to didn't seem to have a clue what was happening.
4 I need a place **to stay** ~~for staying~~ for a few days.
5 Both ~~of~~ / of **the** ideas seem a little hard to put into practice.
6 The woman ~~who~~ / who **is** sitting next to Claire is Frances.
7 Very few ~~of~~ / of **the** people in this country have traveled abroad.
8 The interviewer was impressed by the fact (**that**) ~~how~~ I knew so much about their company.

C

1 most
2 The / That
3 one
4 of
5 their
6 that

9.2 Animal behavior

VOCABULARY

A

1 c 2 f 3 h 4 b 5 g 6 d 7 a 8 e

B

1 gazing 2 fidgeting 3 shrugged 4 shook 5 blinked 6 beckoned 7 pointed 8 raised

GRAMMAR

A

1 Having got/woken up early
2 Despite not knowing
3 Done properly, the job
4 Not being practical, reading the
5 Having just bought a new
6 Given the right

B

1 ~~They were feeling~~ (**Feeling**) threatened, the animals instinctively hid behind the wall.
2 **Having** ~~Had~~ never / **Never having** ~~never~~ been on a plane before, I was both excited and nervous.
3 If ~~you~~ / you **are** successful in your application, you will be notified by email.
4 **Having grown** ~~Grown~~ up in the US, Marvin has always spoken English well.
5 ~~Been~~ (**Being**) exhausted and short on money, Carrie cut short her trip to Bolivia.
6 Before **starting** ~~started~~ work in insurance, Lionel was a factory worker.
7 Despite **not/never having** ~~I hadn't~~ been there before, I soon found my way around.
8 While suffering badly from the flu, **Angela was visited by** a couple of close friends ~~visited Angela~~ every day.

C

1 b 2 c 3 c 4 b 5 a 6 b

9.3 Reading

READING

C

1 T
2 F (They were told this, but the experiment was to see if their behavior was influenced by the words they had processed.)
3 F (They were timed from the moment they finished the task to see how quickly they interrupted, if at all.)
4 T
5 F (The opposite appears to be true – we make major life choices based on similarities of the names of people and things to our own name.)

D

Possible answers

1 to see how long the students would wait before interrupting and to see if students who had been exposed to the 'rude' words interrupted sooner
2 As predicted, students who had been given the 'rude' words interrupted sooner than the others.
3 Bargh himself was reluctant to conclude that exposure to certain types of words makes us behave in that way (because it was a very small sample).

9.4 Listening

LISTENING

C

1 F ('I've lived here for … four years.')
2 T
3 F (Rob says, 'I'd be bummed if I didn't get the grades I want to go to college. … there is a reason behind the pressure.')
4 T
5 T
6 F (The Steiner school has a *'holistic' approach to learning* and doesn't divide it into specific subject areas.)

D

3 I've lived here for … [~~let~~ me see] … ~~for~~ four years.
4 ~~Be~~cause it's [~~you~~ know] … it's really *unique* [~~and~~ stuff].
5 Is it [one ~~of~~] those places where ~~you~~ ~~can~~, [~~you~~ know], do anything you want?

9.5 Write a conclusion to an academic report

WRITING

B

a 3 b 2 c 1 d 4

C

1 c 2 b 3 e 4 a/d 5 d/a

D

Colon (Students underline any two of the following)

'… individual responsibility is ignored: normal values and the ability to reason are abandoned.'

'… convergence theorists argue that individuals in a crowd do not lose personal identity: personal beliefs and values are communicated …'

'... our research revealed that ... in a crowd: crowd catalysts such as police presence ...'

Semi-colon

'... most of the research so far stems from disciplines such as psychology and sociology; there has been little recent research into crowd behavior at large outdoor events.'

'They fail to demonstrate why some crowds ... behave differently; nor do they examine the difference between ...'

WRITING PRACTICE

C

Model answer

Our research attempted to answer the questions of whether the use of slang had increased among the general population in recent years. This proved difficult at first; there is no reliable source of data on the frequency of the use of slang words from before 1970 with which to compare our findings. Nonetheless, we are confident our results relatively accurately reflect the current situation.

There is no doubt that we have been exposed to more informal language and slang since the introduction of the internet and social media, on television and in movies, too. However, our research shows that this is not reflected in the workplace: the average person is not using or exposed to slang more frequently in his/her professional life. In our most recent survey, a larger proportion of the subjects were women; previous surveys were heavily weighted in favor of men. It is clear from the results that women today on average use slang as much as, but not more than, men.

Our research also found that the most frequently used slang expressions have remained much the same for the past 20 years, with newer terms and expressions not yet replacing the older words and phrases in popularity. We suggest that such data be collected periodically to see how the use of individual slang terms changes over time.

In conclusion, our data do not show that the use of slang has increased.

10.1 Urban problems

VOCABULARY

A

1 designated
2 habitats; endangered
3 architectural; heritage
4 ruins; settlement
5 preserve; funds; refurbish

B

1 urge 2 desire 3 responsibility 4 obligation 5 failure
6 refusal 7 tendency 8 reminder

PRONUNCIATION

B

1 up
2 down
3 down
4 up
5 down
6 down
7 up
8 up

GRAMMAR

A

1 h 2 c 3 i 4 b 5 j 6 a 7 g 8 f 9 e 10 d

B

1 despite it being
2 any case, I have
3 namely Australia and China
4 owing to the bad weather
5 whereas the return journey seemed
6 As a matter of fact

10.2 How to change the world

VOCABULARY

A

1 b 2 a 3 c 4 c 5 a 6 c 7 b 8 c

B

1 passionate
2 effective
3 personal
4 persuasive
5 apathetic
6 community

GRAMMAR

A

1 Some people think we can change the world but I don't ~~think we can change the world~~.
2 If you get the opportunity to go, you should ~~take the opportunity to go~~.
3 A lot of people struggle with course fees and I wish they didn't ~~struggle with course fees~~.
4 They should target governments and ~~they should target~~ large companies.
5 We're going to have food and ~~we're going to have~~ music.
6 You asked me if I thought we could make a difference and the answer is yes ~~I do think we can make a difference~~.
7 I know a lot of people who are pessimistic about the future, but I'm not ~~pessimistic about the future~~.
8 ~~Are~~ you joining us for pizza? ~~Do you have~~ any preference ~~as to what we order~~?

B

1 do it / do so
2 he does
3 I do
4 do that/it
5 so
6 do so/that
7 hope not
8 do that

10.3 Reading

READING

A

traffic congestion and the related problem of air pollution

B

Possible answers

	Problems	Solutions	Criticism
UK	Health problems	Workplace parking fee improve public transportation, electric cars	Job losses, strain on public transportation
Paris	Premature deaths	Anti-pollution stickers, fines if no sticker, car manufacturers make non-polluting cars	Few people buy the stickers, people taxed off the road
Freiburg		Pedestrianized city center, cheap and efficient public transportation, prioritize walking, biking and public transportation, incentives for people who don't use cars, good urban planning	

10.4 Listening

LISTENING

B

Possible answers

1 a job interview
2 living in an isolated place
3 the job

C

1 environmental science
2 East
3 two
4 (natural) habitats
5 deer
6 paths
7 preserve
8 endangering
9 research

D

1 When speaking to Dr. Ramsey, Jonathan says 'Hello Dr. Ramsey. How do you do?'
2 When speaking to Dr. Ramsey, Jonathan says 'A glass of water would be great, thank you.'
3 When speaking to Dr. Ramsey, Jonathan says 'I have a degree in environmental science from the University of East Anglia and actually have practical experience from several field trips.'
4 When speaking to Dr. Ramsey, Jonathan says 'I really feel that the job is an ideal opportunity for me and it involves everything that I enjoy doing.'

10.5 Write a persuasive essay

WRITING

B

Possible answers

1 Tourism has a largely negative impact.
2 environmental damage; disrespect for local cultures, traditions and behaviors; lack of benefit for local workers and business
3 Yes. Understanding different cultures; money and job creation

C

1 Paragraph 4
2 Counter-argument: that mass tourism brings economic benefits – more money and more jobs. Rebuttal: the jobs are seasonal, low-skilled and insecure; most of the money goes to large foreign companies, not the local economy.
Yes, the rebuttal directly answers the counter-argument.
3 Counter-argument: 'There is an argument that …'
Rebuttal: 'While this is true up to a point, …'

WRITING PRACTICE

C

Model answer

More and more shopping malls are being built in or near towns and cities all over the world. While some argue that they provide a more convenient and fun shopping 'experience', I would argue that they create a negative impact on local communities which outweighs their convenience.
Perhaps the greatest negative impact of shopping malls is felt by local businesses who, being unable to compete, can lose up to 90% of their business. The community as a whole loses out, because local businesses play an important role in creating community identity.

Shopping malls also have a huge carbon footprint; shopping centers in the US are estimated to create 12 million tons of waste each year, including packaging and food waste. They also waste energy through excessive lighting, day and night, and heat loss through constantly opening doors.

Supporters of shopping mall developments claim that people benefit from the lower prices at malls, somewhere to park, the convenience of being able to do all their shopping under one roof and the fact that malls also provide all kinds of recreational activities, turning shopping into a fun day out for all the family. Yet the concentration of so much in one place brings its own problems, such as increased traffic, pollution, overcrowding and noise.

In summary, the negative effects of shopping malls on local communities outweigh any advantages. They destroy local businesses and community identity, create an enormous amount of waste and have a negative impact on the environment. These are all reasons enough, I believe, to encourage people to shop locally.

Notes

Notes

Notes